# Alan Stevenson

**Publisher**

*Welcome to the **twelfth edition** of my book. The world is now in constant motion with discounted airflights, improved roads (not sure about that one!) and internet access. The ferry across the Forth in the 50's was an adventure itself never mind the rest of your holiday! Remember the queues at the Ballachulish and Kyle Ferries? Recently, a guest at The Summer Isles Hotel where I was also staying told me, "sourced this hotel through your website, took a plane to Glasgow, hired a car and was here in no time." Phew!! Also, guest expectations are changing with more disposable income now than some decades ago. My personal choice reflects such establishments who have managed transition to change but where the comfort of the guest is paramount.*

*Included this year are 5 Michelin star chefs (one with 2 stars) but as with my hotel selection, for one reason or another some, which you may think should be included, have been omitted. Reasons are numerous but should I feel uncomfortable or inhibited, they will not be included. Communication skills are a vital part of this industry – sadly lacking in some quarters I am afraid. My selection this year was somewhat curtailed due to personal family commitments but enjoy your copy of the book – a warm welcome assured.*

*Finally, most grateful to my sponsors for their support, of which a list appears on page 4. Enjoy your journey whereever you go and may the weather be kind to you. My travels for the 2008 edition of my book have commenced already. (Can't wait to get going!) Whether travelling east, west, north or south it never ceases to amaze me how fortunate I am.*

Photo by Yerbury of Edinburgh

# STEVENSONS

## SCOTLAND'S
## GOOD HOTEL AND FOOD BOOK
### 2007

**Published by:**
Alan Stevenson Publications
Fala
20 West Cairn Crescent
Penicuik
Midlothian
EH26 0AR
Tel: 01968 678015
Fax: 01968 679898
**Email: alan@stevensons-scotland.com**
**www.stevensons-scotland.com**

**North American Representative:**
Ann Litt,
Undiscovered Britain
11978 Audubon Place
Philadelphia, PA 19116
Tel: (215) 969-0542
Fax: (215) 969-9251
Email: userann6394@cs.com
www:UndiscoveredBritain.com

**Copyright © 2006 Stevensons - Scotland's Good Hotel and Food Book -
Twelfth Edition**

**ISBN 0 9550877 1 6**

**Price:** £8.00
  $16.00 from USA agent only. (Includes Canada)

**Printed in Scotland:** Woods of Perth Ltd.
**Front Cover:** Culloden House Hotel, Inverness-shire.

# THE SCOTCH BEEF CLUB

# MAKE IT YOUR FIRST CHOICE

We make no apologies for saying restaurants who become members of the Scotch Beef Club are a cut above the rest. Only those who are passionate about serving Scotch Beef to their customers are likely to meet our strict criteria.

Members will be ambassadors for fresh, well produced Scotch Beef. They'll know where it comes from and will be proud to say that it's Scotch.

If you too want to be sure – choose a Scotch Beef Club restaurant.

For an up to the minute list of all UK members visit:

# www.scotchbeefclub.org

Quality Meat Scotland, Rural Centre – West Mains, Ingliston, Newbridge, Midlothian EH28 8NZ
Tel: 0131 472 4040  Fax: 0131 472 4038  Email: info@qmscotland.co.uk

# STEVENSONS

## SCOTLAND'S
## GOOD HOTEL AND FOOD BOOK
## 2007

CONTENTS

# STEVENSONS

## SCOTLAND'S
## GOOD HOTEL AND FOOD BOOK
## 2007

### AWARDS/SYMBOLS

**VisitScotland/Scottish Tourist Board**

The Star System is a world-first. Quality is what determines our star awards, not a checklist of facilities. We've made your priorities our priorities. Quality makes or breaks a visit. This is why it is only the quality of the welcome and service, the food, the hospitality, ambience and the comfort and condition of the property which earns VisitScotland Stars, not the size of the accommodation or the range of available facilities.

The quality grades awarded are:

| ★★★★★ | Exceptional, world-class |
| ★★★★ | Excellent |
| ★★★ | Very Good |
| ★★ | Good |

### AA Red Rosettes 🏵️🏵️🏵️🏵️🏵️

Hotels and restaurants may be awarded red rosettes to denote the quality of food they serve. It is an award scheme, not a classification scheme. They award rosettes annually on a rising scale of one to five.

### AA Red Stars ★★★★★

The AA top hotels in Britain and Ireland are assessed and announced annually with a red star award. They recognise the very best hotels in the country that offer consistently outstanding levels of quality, comfort, cleanliness and comfort care. Red stars are awarded on a rising scale of one to five. Restaurants with rooms also qualify for this award.

### Bull Logo

Any establishment which displays the Bull Logo is a member of the Scotch Beef Club. The criteria is strict - the product is derived from cattle born, reared for all of their lives, slaughtered and dressed in Scotland. The animals will have been produced in accordance with assurance schemes accredited to European Standard and meeting the standards and assessments set by Quality Meat Scotland's Assurance Schemes.

**PLEASE NOTE: THESE AWARDS DO NOT NECESSARILY FORM PART OF MY OVERALL PERSONAL SELECTION OF GOOD HOTELS AND RESTAURANTS IN SCOTLAND. THEY ARE INCLUDED TO ASSIST THE VISITOR SELECT HIS/HER HOTEL OR RESTAURANT OF CHOICE. THE AWARDS ARE NOT MANDATORY FOR SELECTION TO THIS PUBLICATION.**

# DUNVEGAN CASTLE IS NOW OPEN 24 HOURS A DAY ON THE INTERNET.

We are open to the public 7 days a week all year as the major Historic Visitor Attraction on the Isle of Skye. So make Dunvegan Castle "The Must Visit" destination on your Scottish Tour.

**WWW.DUNVEGANCASTLE.COM**

# STEVENSONS

## SCOTLAND'S
## GOOD HOTEL AND FOOD BOOK
## 2007

### HOW TO LOCATE A HOTEL OR RESTAURANT

1. First look at the map of **Scotland** at the beginning of the publication, **on page 9.** The place name of the hotels or restaurants I am featuring will be highlighted in bold type. Restaurants will be highlighted with a red circle. ●

2. Once you have pinpointed your location *follow along the top of the pages*, which are arranged alphabetically, until you arrive at your location.

3. If you already have the name of the hotel or restaurant and wish to know if it is included, turn to the index at the back of the book. Hotels and restaurants are listed alphabetically.

4. In some cases where hotels and restaurants are located close to major towns, they may be shown under that town with the exact location in brackets. For example, **BIGGAR (Skirling)**.

**Culloden House Hotel**

5. **Hotel Price guide:** This quote is based on an overnight stay single & double. Normally this is for bed & breakfast but sometimes if dinner is included it will be indicated. (includes dinner). Also applicable to restaurants with rooms.

6. The above prices are quoted for a one night stay, but most of the establishments in this book offer reductions for stays of two or more nights. Also please enquire about seasonal bargain 'breaks'.

7. **Symbols/Awards.** Awards from VisitScotland (Quality Assurance Classification), AA red food rosettes & stars and the Bull Logo (Scotch Beef Club - Quality Meat Scotland) appear on hotel and restaurant entries. See introductory pages for a full explanation of these symbols and awards.

*Michael Stoddart - Head Chef*
*Marcliffe Hotel, Spa and Restaurant, Aberdeen*

# THE MARCLIFFE HOTEL, SPA AND RESTAURANT

### North Deeside Road, Aberdeen. AB15 9YA
### Tel: 01224 861000   Fax: 01224 868860
Email: reservations@marcliffe.com   www.marcliffe.com

This is an outstanding property perfectly positioned in the attractive 'leafy' suberb of Cults on the outskirts of Aberdeen. Just off the main road to Braemar it is situated in 11 acres of magnificent woodland and garden policies (with ample parking I should add). There are no standard rooms here – bedrooms range from executive rooms to two room suites, and are beautifully appointed. Antique furniture and paintings are a feature, however, modern facilities include satellite TV and modem points. My overnight stay included dinner in the Conservatory Restaurant, menus are sophisticated and chef uses the natural larder on his doorstep to source his ingredients, Aberdeenshire beef, fish and game in season to mention a few. Wine cellar of note to match and bar stocked with over 100 malt whiskies. Ideal to explore the whiskey and castle trails, and never far away from a golf course. New spa and gymnasium  added this year; also health and beauty treatment available. Owned by the Spence Family this hotel is a member of Small Luxury Hotels Of The World and Connoisseurs Scotland. A truly memorable experience.

**Open:** *All year*
**No. Rooms:** *42 En Suite 42*
**Room telephones:** *Yes*
**TV in Rooms:** *Yes*
**Pets:** *Yes*   **Children:** *Yes*
**Disabled:** *Yes*

**Swimming Pool/Health Club:** *Yes (see above)*
**Conference Facilities:** *Extremely good*
**Price Guide:**  *Single £155.00-£295.00 (suite)*
        *Double £175.00 - £295.00 (suite)*
**Location:***Aberdeen ring road, turn west at A93 - to Braemar.*
        *Hotel is 1ml on right. Aberdeen airport 25mins.*

# MELDRUM HOUSE HOTEL (GOLF AND COUNTRY ESTATE)

### Oldmeldrum, Aberdeenshire. AB51 0AE
### Tel: 01651 872294   Fax: 01651 872464
Email: enquiries@meldrumhouse.com   www.meldrumhouse.com

Now owned and under the personal direction of Sylvia Simpson this property has taken on a new lease of life. The transformation has been quite remarkable in such a short space of time – delighted to include Meldrum House Hotel in my personal choice for edition 2007. The hotel is set amongst 350 acres of magnificent woodland and sweeping lawns (carefully manicured) – the golf course and grounds include several water features and an abundance of wildlife. There has been a lot of activity here – all 9 hotel bedrooms are superior in all aspects, en suite bathrooms a delight. Quality furnishings adorn each room. Exceptional venue for weddings with the backdrop of the hotel & grounds – the 4 poster bridal suite is spectacular. Add to this cuisine of an extremely high standard served in the magnificent dining room with faultless service and you really have the complete package. Don't forget the 5 'Chain Lodges' which offer a bit more privacy for that longer stay – also include full Scottish Breakfast. Further development this year includes the conversion of the old stable block to a 'state of the art' conference centre. Enjoyable 2 night stay with great ambience and informed staff. Only a short drive from Aberdeen. Highly recommended.

| | |
|---|---|
| **Open:** *All year* | **Swimming Pool/Health Club:** *No* |
| **No. Rooms:** *14 En Suite 14* | **Conference Facilities:** *Yes* |
| **Room telephones:** *Yes* | **Price Guide:** *Single £100.00 - £130.00* |
| **TV in Rooms:** *Yes* | *Double £120.00-£150.00* |
| **Pets:** *Small dogs* **Children:** *Yes* | **Location:** *Main gates on A947 (Aberdeen to Banff Rd) 1* |
| **Disabled:** *Limited* | *mile north of Oldmeldrum. 13mls north of airport.* |

*AA*

# SUMMER ISLES HOTEL

Achiltibuie, Ross-shire. IV26 2YG
Tel: 01854 622282   Fax: 01854 622251
Email: info@summerisleshotel.co.uk   www.summerisleshotel.co.uk

The road leading to The Summer Isles Hotel at Achiltibuie is 10 miles north of Ullapool. You approach Achiltibuie under the watchful eye of Stac Poly and quite magnificent scenery. The hotel itself commands a delightful spot in the village with spectacular views to The Summer Isles. The Irvine family have run this individual but sophisticated hotel since the late 60's and hosts Mark and Geraldine have established an oasis of civilisation hidden away in stunningly beautiful, but still wild and untouched landscape. This is certainly the place to indulge yourself and Chef Chris Firth-Bernard produces mouth-watering dishes using only locally-sourced ingredients or fish netted nearby. Meal options include dinner at £49.00 (well worth the visit for this alone) or a more informal bar lunch/supper 'around the corner' (seafood a speciality). Bedroom refurbishment continues with the creation of a new 'de-luxe' bedroom within the hotel - personally sampled by myself it was pure indulgence with magnificent views over the isles. The log cabins have all been refurbished (walls knocked down etc) to facilitate the demands of the modern traveller. In my view this hotel is quite unique and exudes peace and contentment in a stunning location. Well worth the visit and highly recommended. **Michelin Star.**

| | | |
|---|---|---|
| **Open:** *6th April - 16th October incl.* | **Disabled:** *No* | **Swimming Pool/Health Club:** *No* |
| **No. Rooms:** *13 En Suite 13* | **Conference Facilities:** *No* | |
| **Room telephones:** *Yes* | **Price Guide:** *Single £78.00-£155.00* | |
| **TV in Rooms:** *Suites and large seaview rooms only* | | *Double from £122.00-£192.00 Suite £252.00* |
| | **Location:** | *A835 to Ullapool. 10 miles north of Ullapool* |
| **Pets:** *By arrangement* **Children:** *Over 8* | | *turn left onto single track road to Achiltibuie. 15 miles to village.* |

# THE AIRDS HOTEL

Port Appin, Appin, Argyll. PA38 4DF
Tel: 01631 730236  Fax: 01631 730535
Email: airds@airds-hotel.com  www.airds-hotel.com

A stunning property overlooking Lismore island the name is well known in hotel circles as one of the premier properties in Scotland. Resident proprietors Shaun and Jenny McKivragan (delightful hosts) continue to uphold the very high standards of hotel keeping. At one time an old ferry inn, it has become a mecca for travellers from all over the world who wish to indulge themselves. All 12 bedrooms are different - tastefully furnished to a high standard. The newly-refurbished cottage (1 king-size & 1 twin plus sofa bed) is proving to be a great success. Prices include breakfast in the hotel and servicing. Seasonal rates apply. Public areas have a 'homely' feel about them with fine artwork on walls and comforting fires conveying an atmosphere of feeling at ease with the world. Diners expectations (Scottish Hotel Chef of the Year, J. Paul Burns) are fully met with a range of dishes executed with high technical skills producing a depth of flavour (good innovation) and use of seasonal produce. Excellent wine list. Sometimes forgotten I was very impressed with the housekeeping - fresh, bright and absolutely spotless. General Manager: Martin Walls. 3 AA red rosettes for food and AA 4 red stars.

| | |
|---|---|
| **Open:** *All year except 3 weeks in Jan* | **Swimming Pool/Health Club:** *No* |
| **No. Rooms:** *12 En Suite + cottage* | **Conference Facilities:** *No* |
| **Room telephones:** *Yes* | **Price Guide:** *Double £245.00-£395.00 Full suite* |
| **TV in Rooms:** *Yes* | *Single £175.00-£285.00 (All include dinner)* |
| **Pets:** *By arrangement* **Children:** *Yes* | **Location:** *20 mls north of Oban on A828. 25 mls* |
| **Disabled:** *2 rms (limited)* | *south of Fort William.* |

Scottish TOURIST BOARD ★★★★ SMALL HOTEL  **AA**🏵🏵🏵 ★★★★

# THE CAIRN LODGE

Orchil Road, Auchterarder, Perthshire. PH3 1LX
Tel: 01764 662634 or 662431    Fax: 01764 664866
Email: info@cairnlodge.co.uk   www.cairnlodge.co.uk

Delighted to include The Cairn Lodge once again – the words 'small but beautiful' aptly describe this 10 bedroomed hotel neatly tucked away within its own private grounds on the south side of Auchterarder not far from the famous Gleneagles Hotel & Resort. The emphasis here is simple – quality and good value for money in an atmosphere of warmth and friendly service. New owner, Ridi Stakis-Christie, which, as the name suggests, has introduced this concept at The Cairn Lodge. All en suite bedrooms are spacious, well appointed and tastefully furnished – all with modern amenities. The dining room has been completely upgraded – ambience perfect. Classical Scottish cuisine – dishes that demonstrate a clear ambition to achieve high standards – good use of fresh quality produce. This is complemented by a fine wine list. Ideal venue with that small wedding or private (get away from it all) corporate meeting in mind. In the heart of this beautiful part of Perthshire  leisure options include golf at the nearby Gleneagles championship course, riding, walking, fishing and a host of other pursuits. Stay awhile and enjoy the Cairn Lodge experience – you will return, of that, I have no doubt.

| | | |
|---|---|---|
| **Open:** *All year* | **Disabled:** *Limited* | |
| **No. Rooms:** *10 En Suite 10* | **Swimming Pool/Health Club:** *No* | |
| **Room telephones:** *Yes* | **Conference Facilities:** *Small - director level* | |
| **TV in Rooms:** *Yes* | **Price Guide:** *Single £85.00 - £140.00* | |
| **Pets:** *To stay in owners' car* | | *Double £115.00-£240.00.* |
| **Children:** *Yes* | **Location:** | *Short drive from Gleneagles.* |

*AA* ✿

# COSSES COUNTRY HOUSE
### Ballantrae, Ayrshire. KA26 0LR
### Tel: 01465 831363   Fax: 01465 831598
Email: info@cossescountryhouse.com   www.cossescountryhouse.com

Despite all the bad weather this year I managed to arrive here on a perfect sunny day with everything in bloom. The attractive 2 mile journey up a farm road from the village, cosseted by hedgerows, sets the tone – here you will find Cosses Country House nestling amongst mature woodland and beautiful gardens. Formerly a shooting lodge dating back to 1606 it was bought by the present owners Robin and Susan Crosthwaite in 1985. Subsequent alterations have made this a haven of peace and tranquility - 12 acres of it. There are 3 elegant and charming bedroom suites with individual décor all on ground floor level – on a cool evening you are drawn to the log fire in the sitting room. Susan's talents extend beyond the garden to the kitchen – her culinary skills are well known and she runs cooking courses and demonstrations during the winter. Ayrshire is renowned for its farming produce and Susan makes excellent use of the local produce combined with vegetables and herbs from her own garden. Restricted menus change on a daily basis but Susan will oblige guests as to their needs if discussed beforehand. Excellent wine list to complement a good meal. Plenty to do and see in this area of Ayrshire and not far from the ferry terminal (Stranraer) for Northern Ireland. Member of the Wolsey Lodge group.

**Open:** *Closed November-February*
**No. Rooms:** *3 En Suite 3*
**Room telephones:** *No*
**TV in Rooms:** *Yes*
**Pets:** *Yes*   **Children:** *Over 12*
**Disabled:** *Not suitable*

**Swimming Pool/Health Club:** *No*
**Conference Facilities:** *No*
**Price Guide:** *Single £40.00 - £47.50 (supp. £15.00) (Dinner £28.00)*
*Double £80.00-£95.00 (Special rates available)*
**Location:**   *From A77 at south end of Ballantrae take inland road at caravan sign. Cosses 2mls on right.*

*Margaret Jaffray*
*Banchory Lodge Hotel*
*40th Anniversary*
*1966-2006*

# BANCHORY LODGE HOTEL

### Banchory, Kincardineshire. AB31 3HS
### Tel: 01330 822625  Fax: 01330 825019
#### Email: enquiries@banchorylodge.co.uk  www.banchorylodge.co.uk

This Deeside hotel which was formerly an 18th century coaching inn is spectacularly situated on the banks of the River Dee. The gardens reflect the care and attention taken by resident proprietor Margaret Jaffray with sweeping lawns down to the river bank and an abundance of flowers (especially the daffodils in spring). This care and attention continues its theme within the hotel where all the best qualities can be savoured. The bedrooms are very spacious and comfortable - designed with considerable flair and imagination. Many have views over the river. The dining room is a masterpiece. Creative menus include Dee salmon and Aberdeen Angus beef as one would expect in this area. Exclusive use of the hotel for weddings (ideal venue) and corporate meetings are welcomed. An old favourite of mine, I have some wonderful memories of this establishment in years past. Margaret will celebrate her 40th anniversary at Banchory Lodge in October 2006. A wonderful tribute to her personally and I have included her portrait this year amongst her beloved garden flowers - always significant displays when you arrive at the hotel.

| | |
|---|---|
| **Open:** *All year* | **Swimming Pool/Health Club:** *No* |
| **No. Rooms:** *22 En Suite 22* | **Conference Facilities:** *Up to 30* |
| **Room telephones:** *Yes* | **Price Guide:** *Single £85.00 Double £150.00* |
| **TV in Rooms:** *Yes* | **Location:** *A93 North Deeside road from Aberdeen.* |
| **Pets:** *Yes* **Children:** *Yes* | *Turn down Dee Street from Main Street -* |
| **Disabled:** *No* | *400 yards - hotel on your left.* |

*By kind permission of Skirling House*

# SKIRLING HOUSE

### Skirling, Biggar, Lanarkshire. ML12 6HD
### Tel: 01899 860274  Fax: 01899 860255
Email: enquiry@skirlinghouse.com  www.skirlinghouse.com

This house, built in 1908, was designed by the famous architect Ramsay Traquair for Lord Carmichael as a country retreat. Skirling is a small attractive village just outside Biggar on the A72 to Peebles and the property is situated by the village green. The house has retained the original theme with carvings, rich fabrics, antiques and fine paintings - a feature is the 16th century Florentine carved ceiling which is much admired by guests. Bob and Isobel Hunter have made this an oasis of great comfort, quality cuisine and hospitality and there is a very informal but friendly and relaxing atmosphere. The award of 5 stars Guest House from VisitScotland is fully merited - bedrooms are tastefully decorated in keeping with the house and offer every comfort. The house menus (dinner is a set menu) change daily and make excellent use of fresh seasonal produce from the garden. Good selection and a sound quality of food with fine farmhouse cheeses. Meals are served in the conservatory with views over the magnificent lawn and gardens to the rear. (also with herb garden) A very skilled operation here and highly recommended. Only a short distance from Edinburgh.

| | | |
|---|---|---|
| **Open:** *March - December* | **Price Guide:** | *Single £77.50-£95.00 (inc. dinner)* |
| **No. Rooms:** *5 En Suite 5* | | *B&B £50.00-£65.00* |
| **Room telephones:** *Yes* | | *Double £135.00-£160.00 (inc. dinner)* |
| **TV in Rooms:** *Yes* | | *B&B £80.00-£100.00* |
| **Pets:** *Yes*  **Children:** *Yes* | **Location:** | *2 mls from Biggar on A72 overlooking* |
| **Disabled:** *Yes* | | *village green.* |

Ian McNaught - Head Chef
*Roman Camp Country House, Callander*
*(3 AA Rosettes)*

# ROMAN CAMP COUNTRY HOUSE

Off Main Street, Callander, Perthshire. FK17 8BG
Tel: 01877 330003  Fax: 01877 331533
Email: mail@romancamphotel.co.uk  www.romancamphotel.co.uk

This is an outstanding property - originally built as a hunting lodge in 1625 for the Dukes of Perth. It is set in 20 acres of beautiful parkland and is well hidden from the main part of the town of Callander offering privacy and isolation. Its geographic position, however, is ideal for touring the Trossachs, which is an area of outstanding beauty in Scotland. Each of the 15 hotel bedrooms has its own distinctive theme with period furniture and all are equipped with the facilities of a VisitScotland 4 Star Hotel. 3 AA rosettes are the hallmark of the cuisine - based on an ever changing menu and the use of fresh local ingredients. Head Chef Ian McNaught maintains a high level of consistency which is the envy of others. The public rooms are a joy with 16th century oak panelling in the library. The spacious dining room, with fine linen and cutlery, is a delight and when required can accomodate a conference or wedding party for up to 100. Resident proprietors Eric and Marion Brown are renowned for their attention to detail and a warm welcome to all.

| | |
|---|---|
| **Open:** *All year* | **Swimming Pool/Health Club:** *No* |
| **No. Rooms:** *15 En Suite 15* | **Conference Facilities:** *Up to 100* |
| **Room telephones:** *Yes* | **Price Guide:** *Single from £75-£140* |
| **TV in Rooms:** *Yes*  **Pets:** *Yes* | *Double from £125-£185* |
| **Children:** *Yes*  **Disabled:** *Yes*  **Location:** | *East End of Callander. Main Street from* |
| **No smoking** | *Stirling turn left down drive for 300 yards.* |

# LOCH NESS LODGE HOTEL

Drumnadrochit, Inverness-shire. IV63 6TU
Tel: 01456 450342   Fax: 01456 450429
Email: info@lochness-hotel.com   www.lochness-hotel.com

Dating back to around 1740, this unusual hotel is synonymous with the famous Loch from which it takes its name. Once the home of a colonial tea planter, it stands in eight acres of delightful woodland grounds. Situated 14 miles from Inverness, it is a favourite spot for tourists. The hotel offers elegant en suite bedrooms and fresh imaginatively prepared food. The restaurant serves a fusion of modern and traditional cuisine: Prime Aberdeen Angus beef, West Coast seafood from Mallaig and Kinlochbervie, local venison, wild mushrooms and fresh garden vegetables. The hotel is linked to the Visitor Centre with its unique exhibition which attracts people from around the world. The management are now actively marketing their corporate facilities - this is the ideal venue for such an occasion away from the 'hustle and bustle' of city life and a short drive from Inverness. Log fires, friendly staff, outstanding cuisine and first class service make a holiday at the Loch Ness Lodge Hotel a memorable experience. Your host : Gillian Skinner.

| | |
|---|---|
| **Open:** *Closed mid Jan - March 1st* | **Swimming Pool/Health Club:** *No* |
| **No. Rooms:** *56 En Suite 56* | **Conference Facilities:** *Max. 120* |
| **Room telephones:** *Yes* | **Price Guide:** *Single £40.00-£60.00* |
| **TV in Rooms:** *Yes* | *Double £80.00-£120.00* |
| **Pets:** *No*   **Children:** *Yes* | **Location:** *14 miles south of Inverness on Fort William* |
| **Disabled:** *Dining only* | *Road.* |

Scottish
TOURIST BOARD
★★★
HOTEL

# THE BUCHANAN ARMS HOTEL & LEISURE CLUB

Drymen, by Loch Lomond, Stirlingshire. G63 0BQ

Tel: 01360 660588   Fax: 01360 660943

(no email or website address available at time of going to press - contact by telephone only)

In the heart of a conservation village   near Loch Lomond, the Buchanan seems to soak up the mood of the beautiful surrounding countryside. A very attractive former coaching inn standing prominent in the picturesque village, it is situated between the vibrant City of Glasgow and historic Stirling, making it the perfect base for touring. The bedrooms, all en-suite, are fresh, bright and spacious. Superior rooms have traditional furnishings, some with four poster beds. Tapestries Restaurant within the Hotel has long had a reputation for good food and convivial surroundings. Service was swift and efficient with some innovative dishes to tempt the palate. The modern leisure facilities are a feature - swimming pool, sauna, jacuzzi, squash courts and 'state-of-the-art' gymnasium and exercise area. The function suite is popular for business meetings, seminars and weddings. This is a 'well rounded' hotel catering for all modern day requirements whether family, business, tourist or simply a very pleasant day out to enjoy afternoon tea. A careful blend of character and comfort.

| | |
|---|---|
| **Open:** *All year* | **Swimming Pool/Health Club:** *Yes* |
| **No. Rooms:** *52 En Suite 52* | **Conference Facilities:** *Up to 150* |
| **Room telephones:** *Yes* | **Price Guide:** *Single from £65.00* |
| **TV in Rooms:** *Yes* | *Double from £110.00* |
| **Pets:** *By arrangement*  **Children:** *Yes* | **Location:**   *Main Street/Drymen by Loch Lomond* |
| **Disabled:** *Limited* | |

*Trevor Brooks - Head Chef*
*Kinnaird, Kinnaird Estate, Dunkeld*
*(3 AA Rosettes)*

# KINNAIRD

Kinnaird Estate, By Dunkeld, Perthshire. PH8 0LB
Tel: 01796 482440   Fax: 01796 482289
Email: enquiry@kinnairdestate.com   www.kinnairdestate.com

A member of the prestigious Relais & Chateaux, Kinnaird is an elegant 17th century country house set on its own 9,000 acre estate overlooking the Tay River valley. With our award-winning chef creating modern classical cuisine and the exquisite décor in the restaurant, Kinnaird offers something special for those wanting that personal touch. All nine double bedrooms are individually and luxuriously decorated and most have a spectacular view of the River Tay. Kinnaird also has a tranquil beauty room called 'the Retreat' where guests can enjoy many different treatments including massage, aromatherapy and facials for pure relaxation. The estate offers salmon and trout fishing on its own private beat, also deer stalking, shooting and walking. This historic house holds a civil license and, with attractive grounds and immaculate gardens, it is perfect for picturesque photographs. With easy access from Edinburgh and Glasgow this makes Kinnaird the perfect venue for small, intimate weddings and meetings.

| | |
|---|---|
| **Open:** *All year* | **Swimming Pool/Health Club:** *No* |
| **No. Rooms:** *9 En Suite 9* | **Conference Facilities:** *Small business meeting Director level* |
| **Room telephones:** *Yes* | **Price Guide:** *Double May-Oct. £475.00 all rooms* |
| **TV in Rooms:** *Yes* | *Nov.-Apr. from £295.00. All rates inc dinner.* |
| **Pets:** *In kennels*   **Children:** *Over 12* | **Location:** *2 miles north of Dunkeld on A9 – take B898* |
| **Disabled:** *Yes* | *turn off.* |

*By kind permission of Ullinish Country Lodge*

# ULLINISH COUNTRY LODGE

### Struan, Isle of Skye, Inverness-shire. IV56 8FD
### Tel: 01470 572214   Fax: 01470 572341
Email: ullinish@theisleofskye.co.uk   www.theisleofskye.co.uk

"Of skerries, sea eagles and wild ocean spray" are the words used as an introduction on the brochure of this stunning six bedroomed establishment – very apt indeed. It was an 'adventure' to return once more this year and experience the 'rebirth' of Ullinish Country Lodge – the investment and effort of resident proprietors Brian and Pamela Howard has been immense. There has been a complete overhaul of the building – the bedrooms (2 with super-king size and 3 with king-size beds) are an absolute delight furnished to an extremely high standard with opulent en suite facilities. The recently awarded 2 AA rosetted restaurant provides dishes of the highest calibre - seared hand dived King Scallop, Oysters, Skye seared salmon, squat lobster confit, Speyside Beef with Chantrelles and puddings to 'die for'. Canapes are served in the comfort of the magnificent lounge before dinner. Head chef Bruce Morrison has made his mark here - his talent and aspirations are clear. His sourcing and preparation demonstrates a clear ambition to drive standards upwards but maintains great consistency with unusual and exciting combinations. Definitely one for the 'foodies'. More recognition to follow I am sure. A short distance to the north is Dunvegan Castle (home of the MacLeods) and to the south Glenbrittle & Portnalong with the Cuillin Hills towering above you. I will return again…and so will you. Highly recommended.

| | |
|---|---|
| **Open:** *All year except Jan* | **Swimming Pool/Health Club:** *No* |
| **No. Rooms:** *6 En Suite 6* | **Conference Facilities:** *No* |
| **Room telephones:** *No* | **Price Guide:** *Single from £90.00* |
| **TV in Rooms:** *Yes* | *Double from £120.00* |
| **Pets:** *No*   **Children:** *Over 16* | **Location:** *9 miles south of Dunvegan on* |
| **Disabled:** *Dining only* | *Sligachan Road* |

*David Williams and the Kitchen Brigade*
*Greywalls, Muirfield, Gullane*
*(3 AA Rosettes)*

# GREYWALLS

Muirfield, Gullane, East Lothian. EH31 2EG

Tel: 01620 842144   Fax: 01620 842241

Email: hotel@greywalls.co.uk   www.greywalls.co.uk

This is truly a magnificent country house designed by Sir Edwin Lutyens only 18 miles east of Edinburgh – the well kept manicured gardens are a paradise for that great escape to peace and contentment. This atmosphere prevails throughout the hotel – bedrooms are opulent to say the least, each one individually furnished and many have fine antiques. This is where you can indulge yourself – public rooms offer every comfort from the comfy panelled library through to the Edwardian Bar where there are a wide range of malt whiskies and brandies. Personally known to me, Head Chef David Williams provides cuisine of the highest quality. He is renowned for his passion and dedicated approach in the kitchen. He brings the best out of good basic ingredients – diners expectations are fully met. Excellent wine list to complement a fine meal. Home of the well known Weaver family, a lodge was built in the late 1960's by Colonel Weaver for his retirement. This lodge is now available for those who wish a bit more privacy and informality and sleeps 1-8 persons (4 good sized bedrooms). Muirfield is synonymous with the open golf championship although there are many courses in the area. Lovely part of East Lothian with sandy beaches and much of Scotland's heritage on your doorstep.

| | |
|---|---|
| **Open:** *Closed January, February* | **Swimming Pool/Health Club:** *No* |
| **No. Rooms:** *23 En Suite 23* | **Conference Facilities:** *Small (Director level)* |
| **Room telephones:** *Yes* | **Price Guide:** *Single £140.00 - £255.00* |
| **TV in Rooms:** *Yes* | *Double £240.00 - £290.00* |
| **Pets:** *By request* | **Location:** *Last turning left after leaving Gullane* |
| **Children:** *Yes* | *travelling East (N. Berwick).* |

# FLODIGARRY COUNTRY HOUSE HOTEL

### Staffin, Isle of Skye, Inverness-shire. IV51 9HZ
### Tel: 01470 552203   Fax: 01470 552301
Email: info@flodigarry.co.uk   www.flodigarry.co.uk

This hotel in the north east corner of Skye near Staffin is situated in a stunning position with the backdrop of the Quiraing mountains and a view to 'die for' across Staffin Bay. The romantic aura of Flodigarry is enhanced with stories of Flora Macdonald and the great escape of Bonnie Prince Charlie from government forces in 1746 following the defeat at the battle of Culloden Moor. Set in glorious woodland and gardens this baronial style mansion house is the perfect 'getaway' from the hustle and bustle of city life. Bedrooms are attractively furnished in keeping with the style of the house and vary from standard to Flagship (4 poster). Flora Macdonald's cottage, in a secluded garden close to the main house and beautifully restored, provides a fascinating step back in time to Scotland's Jacobite past. Candlelit dinners with views over the bay are hugely popular whilst ready meals can be enjoyed in the Bistro Bar. Very relaxed and informal atmosphere with attentive staff. Very romantic place for a wedding – true highland welcome. Weekend group parties including wildlife walks are great fun. Member of the Scotch Beef Club. Host: Robert Cairns.

| | |
|---|---|
| **Open:** *All year.* | **Disabled:** *No* |
| **No. Rooms:** *18 En Suite 18* | **Swimming Pool/Health Club:** *No* |
| **Room telephones:** *Yes* | **Conference Facilities:** *No* |
| **TV in Rooms:** *Optional* | **Price Guide:** *Single p.o.a.* |
| **Pets:** *Yes* | *Double £118.00-£170.00* |
| **Children:** *Yes* | **Location:** *North East of Island - 20mls north of Portree* |

# RAMNEE HOTEL

## Victoria Road, Forres, Moray. IV36 3BN
### Tel: 01309 672410  Fax: 01309 673392
Email: ramneehotel@btconnect.com  www.ramneehotel.net

This fine Edwardian mansion built in 1907 is situated in landscaped gardens to the east of the Royal Burgh of Forres. The Ramnee enjoys a certain amount of isolation but is in easy reach of the town centre which is famous for its parkland floral displays and architectural qualities. I knew this hotel before the arrival of resident director Roy Dinnes but he has brought an expertise with him that has transformed this hotel to a high quality establishment. This is reflected with a VisitScotland 4 star classification. The bedrooms are a delight, (with 4 poster if required) - elegant, and very comfortable, all with en suite facilities - many have views over the Moray Firth. Scottish cuisine with a slight French influence using only the best of local produce - menus are varied to suit your appetite - there is imagination and flair used in the preparation and you will not be disappointed whether dining formally or taking a bar lunch/supper. Golfing is high on the list of sporting activities in this area and businessmen make good use of the conference/seminar facilities. There is a friendly atmosphere which radiates throughout the hotel.

**Open:** *All year.*
**No. Rooms:** *20 En Suite 20*
**Room telephones:** *Yes*
**TV in Rooms:** *Yes*
**Pets:** *Yes* **Children:** *Yes*
**Disabled**: *Unsuitable.*

**Swimming Pool/Health Club:** *No*
**Conference Facilities:** *Theatre up to 100.*
**Price Guide:** *Single £60-£80; Double £75-£120.*
**Location:** *A96 Inverness-Aberdeen off by-pass at roundabout to east side of Forres - 500 yards on right.*

*By kind permission of Inverlochy Castle*

# INVERLOCHY CASTLE
## Torlundy, Fort William. PH33 6SN
### Tel: 01397 702177  Fax: 01397 702953  USA Toll Free Tel: 1-888 424 0106
Email: info@inverlochy.co.uk  www.inverlochycastlehotel.com

This is truly an outstanding property set in magnificent landscaped gardens just North of Fort William. It nestles below Ben Nevis in stunning Highland scenery. Fine decorations throughout befit the Victorian proportions of the rooms and reflect the atmosphere of a former era. Awarded 5 AA red stars and 3 AA red rosettes the cuisine is quite exceptional with food prepared with considerable flair, imagination and originality. As a member of the prestigious Relais & Châteaux this establishment retains all the finest traditions of hotel keeping. A stroll through the walled garden or a spot of fishing in the nearby loch offer relaxation - for the more outgoing there are numerous walks in the area and the ski-ing facilities are some of the best in Scotland. During her visit in 1873 Queen Victoria wrote in her diaries "I never saw a lovelier or more romantic spot". Inverlochy offers its guests a warm welcome, peace and seclusion, with cuisine and wine cellar of the highest standard. **Michelin Star.** (Please mention Stevensons when making reservations). General Manager : Norbert Lieder.

| | |
|---|---|
| **Open:** *All year.* | **Swimming Pool/Health Club:** *No* |
| **No. Rooms:** *18* | **Conference Facilities:** *Yes* |
| **Room telephones:** *Yes* | **Price Guide:** *Single £250-£350; Double/Twin £390-£490;* |
| **TV in Rooms:** *Yes* | *Suite £490-£600.* |
| **Pets:** *Yes* **Children:** *Yes* | **Location:** *3 miles north of Fort William. In the village* |
| **Disabled**: *No.* | *of Torlundy on A82.* |

# BOWFIELD HOTEL AND COUNTRY CLUB

### Howwood, Renfrewshire. PA9 1DZ
### Tel: 01505 705225  Fax: 01505 705230
Email: enquiries@bowfieldcountryclub.co.uk  www.bowfieldcountryclub.co.uk

This hotel and country club is only minutes from Glasgow airport along the A737 - out of town yet within easy reach. Situated in an attractive countryside setting the combination of the hotel and country club merge together perfectly. The hotel has 23 country style cottage bedrooms - all en suite with some nice 'extra touches'. The country club offers a comprehensive range of leisure and fitness facilities - also country club spa with health and beauty treatments. Swimming pool and gym popular with all club members. There are alternative menus depending on whether you require a quick snack or take dinner in the very convivial yet intimate setting of the dining room. The venue is perfect for corporate seminars or weddings. There are 17 golf courses within 25 miles - Loch Lomond within easy reach or visit the historic buildings, museums and art galleries of Glasgow. I really enjoyed my overnight stay here - staff were friendly and efficient. This hotel and country club is refreshingly different - extensive choice and the choice is yours. A very relaxed atmosphere prevalent throughout.

---

**Open:** *All year.*
**No. Rooms:** *23 En Suite 23*
**Room telephones:** *Yes*
**TV in Rooms:** *Yes*
**Pets:** *By arrangement* **Children:** *Yes*
**Disabled**: *Limited*

**Swimming Pool/Health Club:** *Yes. Country spa and beauty treatment*
**Conference Facilities:** *Yes*
**Price Guide:** *Single £85.00 (also enquire about inc. rates)*
*Double £130.00*
**Location:** *A737 from M8 at Glasgow airport. 6 mls exit Howwood (left) onto B787 and follow signs at village to Bowfield at top of the hill*

**AA** ✸ ✸

# HOLIDAY INN THEATRELAND

161 West Nile Street, Glasgow. G1 2RL
Tel: 0141 352 8300   Fax: 0141 332 7447
Email: info@higlasgow.com   www.higlasgow.com

City centre hotels are a rare experience for me but I discovered a real gem at The Holiday Inn Theatreland. As the name indicates it is ideally located next to the Royal Concert Hall and Theatre Royal near George Square. The investment in this property by Maurice Taylor has been massive – a recent refurbishment of all bedrooms has taken place. Hand selected fabrics influenced by the wonderful location in the heart of 'theatreland', fully equipped, with an array of exceptional amenities. Sometimes not associated with 'city hotels' there is a charm and warmth at this establishment – a testament to the skills of management and staff. This ambience prevails throughout – the style of the well known "La Bonne Auberge" hotel restaurant is the envy of others – conceived by Maurice in the 1970's it was 'ahead of its time' – others were to follow. Fine traditional cuisine with a French influence – a la carte or fixed menu available (subject of a separate entry in my Good Food Book). This is a very functional hotel with extremely high standards – ideal for corporate and weddings functions with excellent disabled facilities and ample car parking closeby. The personal touch (lacking in some other establishments) is quite evident here. General Manager: Denis MacCann.

| | |
|---|---|
| **Open:** *All year* | **Swimming Pool/Health Club:** *No* |
| **No. Rooms:** *113 En Suite 113* | **Conference Facilities:** *Up to 100* |
| **Room telephones:** *Yes* | **Price Guide:** *Single room only tariff (see below)* |
| **TV in Rooms:** *Yes* | *Double from £90.00-£175.00 (room only)* |
| **Pets:** *No*  **Children:** *Yes* | *£250.00 (Penthouse)* |
| **Disabled:** *Yes* | **Location:**  *Junction 16 (M8) Opp. Royal Concert Hall* |

# UNRESERVED INDULGENCE

**For further information on products by Gilchrist & Soames please contact:**
•Tel: 01733 384118 •Fax: 01733 384101

# THE PINES

Woodside Avenue, Grantown-On-Spey, Morayshire. PH26 3JR

Tel/Fax: 01479 872092

Email: info@thepinesgrantown.co.uk   www.thepinesgrantown.co.uk

A lovely situation backing directly onto the Wild Woods of Anagach but within a 10 minute walk of the town centre, this small and secluded property is a little gem. The house built in the 19th. century has the atmosphere of a bygone era with fine paintings and antiques. Garden and woodland policies, mainly to the rear, are beautifully landscaped and lead to woodland walks and the famous river Spey – observe nature at first hand in peace and tranquility. Delightful hosts Michael and Gwen Stewart make you feel extremely welcome – more of an ancestral home than a hotel. The bedrooms are all en suite, very comfortable and indeed all are individually furnished and decorated to a very high standard. The dining room with candlelit dinner is the perfect end to the day - Gwen's culinary talents (set menu) provide meals using local quality produce for which this area is renowned. A pre-dinner drink and canapes by the fire in one of the two charming lounges instills that 'feel good' factor. (Plenty of good malts as one would expect in this region). This area is the 'great outdoors' visited by many – golf, fishing, climbing, distilleries and castles could be your choice. The Cairngorm mountains beckon - only 30 minutes from Inverness.

| | |
|---|---|
| **Open:** *March-October* | **Swimming Pool/Health Club:** *No* |
| **No. Rooms:** *7 En Suite 7* | **Conference Facilities:** *Small - on request* |
| **Room telephones:** *No* | **Price Guide:** *Single £55.00-£75.00* |
| **TV in Rooms:** *Yes* | *Double £110.00 – £150.00* |
| **Pets:** *On request* **Children:** *Over 12* | *(reduced rates for 3 days+)* |
| **Disabled:** *Limited* | **Location:** *Entering town take A939 to Tomintoul - first right.* |

# BUNCHREW HOUSE HOTEL

Bunchrew, Inverness. IV3 8TA

Tel: 01463 234917   Fax: 01463 710620

Email: welcome@bunchrew-inverness.co.uk   www.bunchrew-inverness.co.uk

This magnificent, well appointed 17th. century Scottish mansion, is situated just outside Inverness on the shores of the Beauly Firth with breathtaking views of the Black Isle and Ben Wyvis to the north. It is surrounded by 20 acres of beautiful gardens and woodlands. This historic building attracts much interest and was originally built by the 8th. Lord Lovat in 1621. The extremely high standards I have come to know at Bunchrew House Hotel are maintained under the capable supervision of General Manager Gill Omand. Head chef Walter Walker (complete with own vegetable and herb garden) takes great pride in providing traditional Scottish food - his expectations are high and there is a dedicated approach here which I have sampled myself. Well balanced combinations with clear and defined flavours. Accommodation consists of superior and standard suites, some with four poster beds and include all the 'extras'. Apart from the outdoor activities one associates with this area (ski-ing at Aviemore, sailing, cruising, fishing, and golf) there are a number of places of interest to visit including Culloden, Cawdor Castle and Loch Ness). AA 2 Rosettes for food. Well recommended.

| | | |
|---|---|---|
| **Open:** *All year (ex. Xmas)* | **Swimming Pool/Health Club:** *No* | |
| **No. Rooms:** *16 En Suite 16* | **Conference Facilities:** *up to 80* | |
| **Room telephones:** *Yes* | **Price Guide:** *Single from £95.00* | |
| **TV in Rooms:** *Yes* | *Double from £140.00-£230.00* | |
| **Pets:** *No*   **Children:** *Yes* | **Location:** *3 miles outside city on A862 Beauly Road* | |
| **Disabled:** *Yes* | | |

# CULLODEN HOUSE HOTEL

### Culloden, Inverness. IV2 7BZ
### Tel: 01463 790461    Fax: 01463 792181
Email: info@cullodenhouse.co.uk   www.cullodenhouse.co.uk

Quite a majestic entrance to this property – a very stately mansion with all the 'trappings' of Bonnie Prince Charlie and the last battle on British soil in April 1746. The sweeping manicured lawns and building-clad virginia creeper cannot fail to impress the visitor and rightly so – the current 'Bonnie Prince Charlie' has been a visitor here of course. Within the elegance and charm of this hotel is true Highland hospitality – guests are met with a genuine welcome – there is a very friendly and relaxed atmosphere which immediately puts you at ease. It is testament to the hard work of Operation Director, Stephen Davies and his mother Patricia (permanent fixture here for 12 years) that this hotel operates so well. Talented and devoted head chef Michael Simpson (20 years) is known by reputation for his culinary skills and holds the 2 AA red rosette award. Spacious and comfortable bedrooms (some suites) each uniquely decorated – in addition the Garden Pavilion closeby with 4 luxury suites which offer seclusion. Romantic setting for a wedding or indeed a private corporate meeting. The City of Inverness has itself a lot to offer the visitor – there are also a number of visitor and historical attractions in the area. (Also see front cover). Airport 15 minutes. Highly recommended.

| | |
|---|---|
| **Open:** *All year* | **Swimming Pool/Health Club:** *No* |
| **No. Rooms:** *28 En Suite 28* | **Conference Facilities:** *Up to 40* |
| **Room telephones:** *Yes* | **Price Guide:** *Single £155.00-£189.00* |
| **TV in Rooms:** *Yes* | *Double £210.00-£290.00 (suite)* |
| **Pets:** *Yes*   **Children:** *Yes* | *Enquire about seasonal breaks* |
| **Disabled:** *Not suitable* | **Location:** *3mls from Inverness & 3mls from airport* |

# KINCRAIG HOUSE HOTEL

by Invergordon, Ross-shire. IV18 0LF
Tel: 01349 852587   Fax: 01349 852193
Email: info@kincraig-house-hotel.co.uk   www.kincraig-house-hotel.co.uk

This Georgian-style building of great character stands in 5 acres of well groomed parkland overlooking the Cromarty Firth – just a short drive North from Inverness on the A9. Already 4 star rated by VisitScotland this is truly a magnificent property propelled by the vision of the owners at The Cuillin Hills Hotel on the Isle of Skye (see separate entry under Portree). No expense has been spared with the comfort of the guest a priority – great care has been taken with the refurbishment of each bedroom, each with its own distinctive charm. Premier bedrooms offer that little bit extra comfort – all spacious, with superior en suite amenities and views over the garden. The large oak-panelled lounge has been retained virtually as it was in a bygone era, sumptuous sofas and chairs with that cosy feeling complete with log fire – the Adam fireplace in the lounge bar a favourite. The atmosphere of well being prevails throughout the hotel – the restaurant (bar meals are available) provides cuisine of the highest quality from their table d'hote menu - service efficient and friendly. This hotel is the perfect retreat with golf courses from Inverness to Brora and Royal Dornoch, sandy beaches, castles and distilleries – or just relax reading a book. You will not be disappointed.

| | |
|---|---|
| **Open:** *All year* | **Swimming Pool/Health Club:** *No* |
| **No. Rooms:** *15 En Suite 15* | **Conference Facilities:** *Up to 48* |
| **Room telephones:** *Yes* | **Price Guide:** *Single from £55.00-£85.00* |
| **TV in Rooms:** *Yes* | *Double from £130.00-£170.00* |
| **Pets:** *No*   **Children:** *Yes* | **Location:**  *20 miles beyond Inverness on A9, 1 mile past* |
| **Disabled:** *1 Room + Dining* | *Alness on left.* |

# THE STEADINGS AT THE GROUSE & TROUT

Flichity, Farr, Inverness-shire. IV2 6XD

Tel: 01808 521314   Fax: 01808 521741

Email: stay@steadingshotel.co.uk   www.steadingshotel.co.uk

This building, formerly farm steadngs built in 1860, is located  only 8 miles from Daviot on the A9 just south of Inverness. (B851 scenic route to Fort Augustus) Here in Upper Strathnairn the hotel is set amidst the magnificent scenery of lochs and heather and contained within well kept garden policies – a building of great character with rustic stonework and timber beams. My visit here was prompted by the arrival of new owners David & Mary Allen who were known to me from a previous time. The planned refurbishment has already commenced. (and it was required) Bedrooms have already been upgraded – all ensuite with modern amenities and extra personal 'touches'. Experienced in culinary matters David has introduced well balanced and interesting menus – uncomplicated but wholesome dishes. Game shooting, loch/river/sea fishing and golf can be arranged. Peace and quiet away from the city life but just a short distance from Inverness. Historic castles, and landmarks are too numerous to mention – Culloden battlefield just up the road and Loch Ness a short distance away. Keep an eye on this one – more to report next year I am sure.

| | | |
|---|---|---|
| **Open:** *Mar-Dec.* | **Swimming Pool/Health Club:** *No* | |
| **No. Rooms:** *9 En Suite* | **Conference Facilities:** *Up to 10* | |
| **Room telephones:** *No* **TV in Rooms:** *Yes* | **Price Guide:** *Single £55.00* | |
| **Pets:** *Yes (by arrangement)* | *Double £95.00* | |
| **Children:** *Yes (by arrangement)* | **Location:** | *Strathnairn between Farr & Croachy. 5mls* |
| **Disabled:** *Yes (dining only)* | | *sth of Inverness take B851 to Ft. Augustus.* |

Jonny Greer - Head Chef
*Ballathie House*

# BALLATHIE HOUSE

Kinclaven, By Stanley, Perthshire. PH1 4QN
Tel: 01250 883268   Fax: 01250 883396
Email address: email@ballathiehousehotel.com   www.ballathiehousehotel.com

Ballathie House is a short drive from Perth and situated in its own country estate setting overlooking the River Tay. The main driveway is an experience in itself with sweeping lawns and magnificent gardens stretching down to the river. This house of character dates back to 1850. The original public rooms have retained all the elegance of a country house in the true sense of the word - fine antique furnishings and period bathrooms. Premier and standard bedrooms within the main house have all been upgraded and reflect a very high quality of accommodation with all modern facilities. The sensitive development of the new riverside rooms & suites, all with views over the Tay, have proved a great success. The Sportsman's lodge rooms (en suite) and one self-catering apartment are now complete. Every comfort here for the fishing/sportsmen with use of all main house facilities. Enquiries via main hotel reception. Exciting times ahead in the kitchen with Jonny Greer (see facing page) recently promoted to head chef ably assisted by Iain Dunn (new sous chef). New dishes and combinations may be introduced with some innovation - both chefs are known to me and both will maintain (even exceed) the reputation that Ballathie has as an excellent food destination. Highly recommended and once you have visited I can assure you, you will return. Your host at Ballathie is Chris Longden.

| | |
|---|---|
| **Open:** *All year* | **Swimming Pool/Health Club:** *No* |
| **No. Rooms:** *42 En Suite 42* | **Conference Facilities:** *Boardroom meetings to 30* |
| **Room telephones:** *Yes* | **Price Guide:** *Single from £85.00 Double £170.00-£230.00* |
| **TV in Rooms:** *Yes* | *2 Day breaks from £89.00 P.P.P.N., D.B.B.* |
| **Pets:** *Yes*  **Children:** *Yes* | **Location:** *Off A9, 2 miles North of Perth through Stanley/or* |
| **Disabled:** *Yes* | *off A93 at Beech hedge and signs.* |

# THE FOUR SEASONS HOTEL
## St. Fillans, Perthshire. PH6 2NF
### Tel: 01764 685333   Fax: 01764 685444
Email:info@thefourseasonshotel.co.uk   www.thefourseasonshotel.co.uk

Aptly named for the ever changing weather patterns, this hotel has one of the finest lochside locations in Scotland. Its position looking south west down Loch Earn must be the envy of others set amongst scenic mountains and woodland. Snugly positioned at the west end of the village the panoramic views are magnificent. "With food to match" - quote from resident proprietor Andrew Low whose experience in culinary matters are not unknown. A solid 2 AA rosette food award the kitchen was upgraded in 2004 and menus changed. I chose to dine formally in the Meal Reamhar Restaurant. A more informal meal can be taken in the Tarken Room - same quality evident. Excellent wine list to complement a good meal and finish your day with a malt around a log fire. Bedrooms are spacious and comfortable - most overlook the loch - plus 6 holiday chalets at the rear of the hotel offer more privacy. Leisure activities are too numerous to mention. The hotel can provide first class facilities for small meetings or functions and Andrew holds a wedding licence for that special day. Good atmosphere here - laid back as described in the hotel brochure. Good value for money. Enjoyed my overnight stay.

| | |
|---|---|
| **Open:** *March - December inclusive* | **Swimming Pool/Health Club:** *No* |
| **No. Rooms:** *12 En Suite 12; 6 chalets* | **Conference Facilities:** *Up to 36* |
| **Room telephones:** *Yes* | **Price Guide:** *Single £48.00-£83.00* |
| **TV in Rooms:** *Yes* | *Double £96.00-£116.00* |
| **Pets:** *Yes* **Children:** *Yes* | *Chalets £44.00-£88-00* |
| **Disabled**: *No* | **Location:** *A85 - west end of St. Fillans village.* |

Scottish
TOURIST BOARD
★★★
SMALL
HOTEL

*AA* ✿ ✿

# INVER LODGE HOTEL

Lochinver, Sutherland. IV27 4LU
Tel: 01571 844496   Fax: 01571 844395

Email: stay@inverlodge.com   www.inverlodge.com

Owned by the Vestey family (who have been in this area since 1930) this superb and modern hotel was opened in 1988 - the quote "don't judge a book by its cover" is very apt here. The exterior of the building presents a complete contrast to its wild highland surroundings but do not be dismayed - I have stayed here for 12 consecutive years and like me you will return once you have sampled the hospitality at Inver Lodge. All 20 bedrooms and the dining room have views over Loch Inver Bay - the sunsets are spectacular. Public rooms, bedrooms and dining room are all extremely spacious and furnished to a very high standard - there are 2 suites. Executive chef, Peter Cullen displays great technical skills in the kitchen - good use of fresh local produce with a regular visit to the harbour every morning. Daily changing menu with an excellent choice of fish, meat and game. Wild mushrooms in season a speciality. It is a true testament to the General Manager  Nicholas Gorton and his team that such high standards have been maintained over so many years - the service cannot be faulted - the comfort of the guest is paramount. 2 smoking bedrooms available. Elevated to 4 AA red stars this year.

| | |
|---|---|
| **Open:** *Early April-end Oct.* | **Swimming Pool/Health Club:** *Sauna* |
| **No. Rooms:** *20 En Suite 20* | **Conference Facilities:** *No* |
| **Room telephones:** *Yes* | **Price Guide:** *Single £100.00 Double from £160.00* |
| **TV in Rooms:** *Yes* | **Location:** *Through village on A835 and turn left after* |
| **Pets:** *Yes*   **Children:** *Yes* | *village hall.* |
| **Disabled:** *Unsuitable* | |

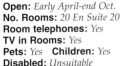

# MELFORT PIER & HARBOUR

### Kilmelford, by Oban, Argyll. PA34 4XD
### Tel: 01852 200333   Fax: 01852 200329
Email: melharbour@aol.com   www.mellowmelfort.com

Why rent a room when you can pamper yourself in the privacy of your own luxury lochside house, each with its own sauna, spa bath, gourmet kitchen and underfloor heating. Most with ensuite bathrooms, log fire and laundry facilities. Bring your own boat and fishing equipment. Free fishing from the pier and use of a Canadian canoe and rowboat. There is a restaurant/bistro on site serving local fresh food and the best coffee! Also a small shop with the 'essentials' and cooked breakfast all day. Come and sit on one of our private beaches and observe the tranquility and totally unwind. Dogs and children of any age are very welcome. Dog and baby-sitting services available. Houses have 1, 2 or 3 bedrooms, all to a Scandinavian design and finished to the highest standards providing freedom, flexibility and luxury. Leisure activities include fishing, watersports, hill-walking and wildlife watching. Nearby horse-riding, golf, stalking, diving and great shopping. Stay two nights or a week and just relax and rejuvenate - choose the things you want to do, when you want to do them. Six of the houses are for Category 2 disabled, all on one floor and with ramps. Walk-in showers and even a sauna suitable for wheelchairs. Parking right in front of your house.

| | |
|---|---|
| **Open:** *All year (7 days a week)* | **Swimming Pool/Health Club:** *Sauna & Spa Bath in each house* |
| **No. Houses:** *15 En Suite 15 + houses* | **Conference Facilities:** *Up to 48* |
| **House telephones:** *Yes email hook-up* | **Price Guide:** *Single: £45.00–£75.00; Double: £90.00-£150.00* |
| **TV in House:** *Yes Satellite* | *2/3 bedroomed houses: £140.00-£230.00* |
| **Pets:** *2 per house* **Children:** *Yes* | **Location:** *On A816 18 miles north of Lochgilphead or 16 miles south* |
| **Disabled:** *Cat. 2. VisitScotland* | *of Oban – 1¹/₂ miles off main road. Well signposted* |

# GLENMORISTON ARMS HOTEL AND RESTAURANT

## Invermoriston, by Loch Ness, Inverness-shire. IV63 7YA
### Tel: 01320 351206   Fax: 01320 351308

Email: reception@glenmoristonarms.co.uk   www.glenmoristonarms.co.uk

Dating back to 1740, this former drovers inn is located in the heart of the village of Invermoriston just a short stroll from the world famous Loch Ness. It enjoys an excellent location situated on the crossroads of the gateway to Skye and the islands but also midway between Fort William and Inverness. This certainly follows through as the hotel's motto is 'in the middle of nowhere, but in the centre of everything'. The attractive profusion of flowers and shrubs enhance the property - the new vegetable and herb garden is now complete. The a la carte menu offers an excellent choice of traditional Scottish dishes, from Aberdeen Angus to occasional delights such as Scottish border ostrich and resident head chef Graham Smith will strive to make your visit a delight when you dine in this AA 2 red rosette rated restaurant. "The quintessential Scottish break everyone should have," remarked a guest - such is the ambience of the hotel. The Moriston Bar now contains over 140 single malt whiskies plus a very extensive and sophisticated wine list. Currently, only 8 en suite rooms, attention to detail is paramount. Owners Nik & Hazel Hammond play a very 'hands on' role in the running of the hotel with a genuine warm welcome to all. Excellent value for money.

| | |
|---|---|
| **Open:** *All year except Jan & Feb* | **Swimming Pool/Health Club:** *No* |
| **No. Rooms:** *8 En Suite 8* | **Conference Facilities:** *No* |
| **Room telephones:** *Yes* | **Price Guide:** *Single £60.00-£75.00  Double £90.00-£150.00* |
| **TV in Rooms:** *Yes* | *Four Poster £150.00* |
| **Pets:** *No*  **Children:** *Yes* | **Location:**  *Midway between Inverness and Fort William* |
| **Disabled:** *No* | *on A82 - hotel in village of Invermoriston* |

# LADYBURN

**By Maybole, Ayshire. KA19 7SG**
**Tel: 01655 740585   Fax: 01655 740580**
Email: jh@ladyburn.co.uk   www.ladyburn.co.uk

An elegant private and secluded country house hotel in a most attractive rural setting, surrounded by mature wild and formal gardens. Described by owner Jane Hepburn as "the most beautiful valley in Ayrshire" this charming property provides gracious living enjoyed by previous generations in a very intimate but relaxed style. Antiques and fine furniture throughout the house, the principal bedrooms each with its own distinct character, luxurious and some with views over lawns and garden. A 'Granny Flat' which sleeps four is an option here – own front door or entrance direct to the house and would suit parents with children. Although a restricted menu (no a la carte) Jane will endeavour to please all dietary requirements and guests can suggest favourites. A real dining experience here – Jane is well known for her excellent use of local (Ayrshire) produce. Excellent wine list. Jane & Catriona (daughter) display a total commitment to the comfort of their guests.  A member of Scotland's Garden Scheme with 4 rose collections this is a perfect retreat. Turnberry & Troon open golf championship courses within easy reach – maybe a visit to Culzean Castle or the birth place of Robert Burns. Romantic venue for small weddings (licensed). AA 2 red stars, AA rosette.

| | |
|---|---|
| **Open:** *April-October*<br>*Restricted November-March*<br>**No. Rooms:** *5 En Suite 5*<br>**Room telephones:** *Yes*<br>**TV in Rooms:** *Yes*<br>**Pets:** *No*   **Children:** *Over 16 in hotel*<br>**Disabled:** *Not suitable* | **Swimming Pool/Health Club:** *No*<br>**Conference Facilities:** *Small - up to 12*<br>**Price Guide:** *Single from £80.00 Double from £160.00*<br>*Dinner from £32.50*<br>**Location:** *12mls south of Ayr. Use A77 to Maybole, B7023 to Crosshill. Right at war memorial - exactly 2mls left - 3/4ml down lane on right - no signs.* |

# BURTS HOTEL

Market Square, Melrose, Roxburghshire. TD6 9PN
Tel: 01896 822285   Fax: 01896 822870
Email: burtshotel@aol.com   www.burtshotel.co.uk

Built in 1722 Burts Hotel nestles in the shadow of the Eildon Hills in the very heart of the Scottish Borders – the famous Greenyards rugby ground closeby. Known to me for more years than I wish to mention the Henderson family have operated this hotel for the past 34 years. Graham & Anne Henderson have built up an enviable reputation – now maintained by sons Nicholas & James. The 20 en suite bedrooms are exceptional offering every comfort and amenities for the modern day traveller. Dining in the elegant restaurant or a more informal setting in the bar could be your choice. Emphasis on fresh ingredients prepared with skill and flair – some innovative choices on the bar menu. AA 2 rosette award and recommended by other food guides of note. Melrose and the borders are enriched with stories of Scotland's past and there are a number of abbeys, stately homes and gardens to visit. Golf courses within easy reach – salmon and trout fishing can be arranged on the famous River Tweed. The welcome addition of The Townhouse directly opposite creates the perfect partner for Burts Hotel – ideal for corporate, private functions or business meetings. Member of The Scotch Beef Club.

| | |
|---|---|
| **Open:** *All year exc. Boxing Day* | **Swimming Pool/Health Club:** *No* |
| **No. Rooms:** *20 En Suite 20* | **Conference Facilities:** *Up to 40* |
| **Room telephones:** *Yes* | **Price Guide:** *Single from £55.00* |
| **TV in Rooms:** *Yes* | *Double £100.00 - £120.00* |
| **Pets:** *Yes*    **Children:** *Yes* | **Location:** *A6091, 2 miles from A68, 38 miles south* |
| **Disabled:** *Limited* | *of Edinburgh.* |

# THE BUCCLEUCH ARMS HOTEL
## High Street, Moffat, Dumfries. DG10 9ET
### Tel: 01683 220003   Fax: 01683 221291
Email: enquiries@buccleucharmshotel.com   www.buccleucharmshotel.com

Again this year the Smith family have exceeded all expectations and are now firmly established as a leading player in the area of Moffat and border region of Scotland. A family hotel in the true sense of the word (too numerous to mention here) there is a distinct 'buzz' about the hotel – a quiet efficiency to every detail and a very warm welcome. Awards and recognition are coming their way – Executive chef Lara Smith whose background includes some of the top hotels in South Africa, supervises menus and dishes which clearly indicate a dedication and knowledge of the industry. Quality sourcing of ingredients from this rich agricultural area of Scotland and some from further afield. Culinary skills do the rest. The refurbishment of the upstairs dining room creates the perfect ambience. Bedrooms are en suite and offer every comfort – downstairs the lounge/bar area is ideal for the pre-dinner apertif and a good 'blether'. Staff (training here is obvious) treat guests with courtesy and at all times are extremely attentive and helpful. The high standards set by the Smith family will be maintained I have no doubt. Customer expectations are fully met. Come and relax at this famous border town – lots to see and do – excellent value for money. Very active members of the Scotch Beef Club.

| | |
|---|---|
| **Open:** *All year* | **Disabled**: *No* |
| **No. Rooms:** *18 En Suite 18* | **Swimming Pool/Health Club:** *No* |
| **Room telephones:** *No* | **Conference Facilities:** *Up to 60* |
| **TV in Rooms:** *Yes* | **Price Guide:** *Single from £50.00* |
| **Pets:** *Yes* | *Double from £80.00* |
| **Children:** *Yes* | **Location:** *Moffat - High Street* |

# KIRROUGHTREE HOUSE

Newton Stewart, Wigtownshire DG8 6AN
Tel: 01671 402141   Fax: 01671 402425
Email: info@kirroughtreehouse.co.uk   www.kirroughtreehouse.co.uk

This award winning hotel stands in 8 acres of beautiful landscaped gardens of which rhododendrons are a feature. This mansion house hotel depicts all that is excellent in the finest traditions of hotel keeping. The building has been restored and refurbished in keeping with the character of the building – the rooms are spacious and very comfortable with en suite facilities. Varying degrees of comfort range from standard, de luxe and the opulent regal suite. All are elegant in their own right – the word elegance can also be used to describe the wonderful panelled lounge and 2 dining rooms. The qualities of head chef Rolf Mueller (Master Chef of Great Britian) are obvious – using only the best of local produce he prepares dishes which have earned him and the hotel 2 AA red rosettes. Menus are short but with sufficient choice and are very creative. The McMillan family are rightly proud of their efforts at Kirroughtree. Highly recommended.

| | |
|---|---|
| **Open:** *Feb 14-Jan 3* | **Swimming Pool/Health Club:** *No* |
| **No. Rooms:** *17 En Suite 17* | **Conference Facilities:** *Max 20* |
| **Room telephones:** *Yes* | **Price Guide:** *Single £95.00-£105.00* |
| **TV in Rooms:** *Yes* | *Double £170.00-£210.00* |
| **Pets:** *By arrangement*  **Children:** *Over 10* | **Location:** *From A75 take A712 New Galloway* |
| **Disabled:** *Unsuitable* | *Road. Hotel 300 yards on left.* |

# HEBRIDEAN PRINCESS

Kintail House, Skipton, N. Yorks. BD23 2DE
Tel: 01756 704704   Fax: 01756 704734
Email: reservation@hebridean.co.uk   www.hebridean.co.uk

From the port of Oban, experience the most beautiful scenery of the British Isles aboard the luxurious Hebridean Princess. This small and unique cruise ship with immaculately maintained teak decks and polished brass, cruises through the Western Isles of Scotland and across the Irish Sea in inimitable style. The epitome of understated elegance, from the panoramic Tiree Lounge to the plush Columba Restaurant, the public rooms and 30 spacious cabins are beautifully designed and decorated throughout. Imaginative menus are created using the freshest local produce to bring you memorable breakfasts and elegant dining, with first class service from one of the best crews afloat. Hebridean Princess sails Scotland's western isles between March and November, with a maximum of just 49 guests. During 18 seasons she has explored some of Scotland's most remote regions, sailing as far west as far-flung St Kilda, and north to the Orkneys and Shetlands. In 2006 her programme also includes 3 cruises along the east coast of Ireland and in August she voyages to Norway to cruise the fjords north and south of Bergen.

| | |
|---|---|
| **Open:** *March to November* | **Swimming Pool/Health Club:** *No* |
| **No. Cabins:** *30 En Suite 30* | **Conference Facilities:** *No* |
| **TV in Rooms:** *Yes* | **Price Guide:** *7 night all-inclusive cruise from* |
| **Pets:** *No* | *£1470.00 per person.* |
| **Children:** *Aged 9 and over* | **Location:**   *Sails from Oban* |
| **Disabled:** *No* | |

# THE MANOR HOUSE
### Gallanach Road, Oban, Argyll. PA34 4LS
### Tel: 01631 562087   Fax: 01631 563053
Email: info@manorhouseoban.com   www.manorhouseoban.com

On the outskirts of Oban just beyond the ferry terminal this Georgian House, built in 1780 commands an enviable position overlooking the Oban bay to the islands beyond. Known to me for many years it is situated in a quiet spot away from the main centre of Oban and retains the charm and elegance of a bygone era. Under the personal supervision of General Manager Ann MacEachen, this small hotel offers every comfort one would expect from a VisitScotland 4 star rating and cuisine to match. Bedrooms are extremely comfortable (some with views over the bay), public rooms are spacious, well furnished and cosy with log fire in the winter (when I stayed). The restaurant is a delight – well known for its use of fresh local produce. Fresh fish (as one would expect) lamb and game in season could be your choice. Ideal stay for a day journey to the island of Mull or explore the beautiful Argyll coastland north or south of Oban. Breath-taking views from many points along the way. AA one rosette for food. A favourite with many over the years.

| | |
|---|---|
| **Open:** *All year except Christmas* | **Swimming Pool/Health Club:** *No* |
| **No. Rooms:** *11 En Suite 11* | **Conference Facilities:** *No* |
| **Room telephones:** *Yes* | **Price Guide:** *Single  £100.00 – £167.00 (includes dinner)* |
| **TV in Rooms:** *Yes* | *Double  £150.00 – £224.00 (includes dinner)* |
| **Pets:** *By request*  **Children:** *Over 12* | *Enquire about seasonal breaks.* |
| **Disabled:** *No* | **Location:**  *200yds past ferry terminal on Gallanach Road.* |

**AA**

# CRINGLETIE HOUSE

### Peebles, Peeblesshire. EH45 8PL
### Tel: 01721 725750  Fax: 01721 725751
#### Email: enquiries@cringletie.com  www.cringletie.com

Elegance and charm would describe Cringletie House with magnificent gardens, sweeping lawns and walled garden. Just 15 miles south of Edinburgh this baronial mansion stands proudly above Eddleston Water with views over the Moorfoot hills. Owners Jacob & Johanna van Houdt take an immense pride in what they do here – a lot of hard work and a complete refurbishment of the property and this establishment takes its rightful place as a premier destination. Every detail has been meticulously planned from basement to the top floor. Bedrooms exude comfort – quality furnishings and drapes. The large disabled room on the ground floor is 'state of the art' – a modern lift (speaks to you) has been installed to transport you to other parts - lounge bar, leading to the spacious conservatory has been designed to offer comfort and that homely feeling with burning log fire and a fine range of malt whiskies. The kitchen brigade demonstrate a dedicated approach – high technical skills here with seasonal fresh ingredients from local suppliers and garden. (AA 2 rosettes) Ideal venue for that small wedding (50-60) or corporate meetings. This is the complete experience so indulge yourself and enjoy. Pride of Britain member. General Manager: Jeremy Osborne.

| | |
|---|---|
| **Open:** *All year* | **Swimming Pool/Health Club:** *No* |
| **No. Rooms:** *14 En Suite 14* | **Conference Facilities:** *50-60* |
| **Room telephones:** *Yes* | **Price Guide:** *Single from* **£95.00** *for standard room* |
| **TV in Rooms:** *Yes* | *Double from* **£115.00** *for standard room (pppn)* |
| **Pets:** *Restricted*  **Children:** *Yes* | *DBB available + seasonal breaks* |
| **Disabled:** *Yes - 1 room* | **Location:**  *From Peebles take A703 north – 2 miles on left.* |

Scottish TOURIST BOARD ★★★★ SMALL HOTEL

**AA** ❀❀

★★★★

# PARKLANDS HOTEL & RESTAURANT

2 St. Leonard's Bank, Perth. PH2 8EB
Tel: 01738 622451   Fax: 01738 622046
Email: info@theparklandshotel.com   www.theparklandshotel.com

Just on the periphery of central Perth overlooking the South Inch this classical town house has a country feel about it. Formerly the home of John Pullar, Lord Provost of Perth from 1867 to 1873 it has retained all its classical lines enhanced by very attractive gardens. With a lot of hard work and investment owners Scott and Penny Edwards have completely refurbished (could even use the word overhaul) this hotel and is now one of the leading players in Perth. Head chef Graeme Pallister (known to me from previous regimes) displays great technical skills in the kitchen. Both classical and modern, excellent use of seasonal produce and clear well-defined flavours. His consistency has now earned him 2 AA red rosettes. There is a quiet efficiency here – excellent service and attention to detail. This is a popular venue for corporate meetings or even a wedding! The hotel imparts a relaxed and friendly atmosphere – not far from the town centre there are a number of historical attractions to see – Scone closeby has strong connections with the dynasty of Scottish Kings. A lot to do and see so prolong your stay. 4 star VisitScotland.

| | |
|---|---|
| **Open:** *All year* | **Swimming Pool/Health Club:** *No* |
| **No. Rooms:** *14 En Suite 14* | **Conference Facilities:** *Up to 24* |
| **Room telephones:** *Yes* | **Price Guide:** *Single £89.00-£119.00 (enquire about seasonal breaks)* |
| **TV in Rooms:** *Yes* | *Double from £109.00-£169.00* |
| **Pets:** *Yes*  **Children:** *Yes* | **Location:** *From A90 head towards railway station.* |
| **Disabled:** *Dining only* | *Parklands on left at end of South Inch* |

*AA* ❀ ❀

# POOL HOUSE

**Poolewe, By Achnasheen, Wester Ross. IV22 2LD**
**Tel: 01445 781272  Fax: 01445 781403**
Email: enquiries@poolhousehotel.com  www.poolhousehotel.com

This is a stunning property, in a stunning location that has been transformed over the years – the opulence of the well proportioned bedrooms, the fine cuisine, the home baking with extremely friendly and efficient service could not be faulted. Complete indulgement rarely found in this part of the highlands. The Harrison family have created the perfect retreat (not without a lot of hard work and planning I should add) amongst some of Scotland's most scenic and rugged landscape on the shores of Loch Ewe. The themed suites are magnificent in every detail – the ensuite bathrooms a real feature of a bygone era. Dining here is a marvellous experience – the ambience of the dining room which overlooks Loch Ewe is perfect – the cuisine, mainly sourced from the abundance of fresh local produce demonstrates a clear ambition to achieve high standards. I have stayed here on a few occasions and monitored the progress. The exclusive use of this property is a clear option – incentive 'breaks' for corporate or private use. Boat trips, nature trails (Inverewe Gardens closeby) walking and falconry can all be arranged. This Victorian house has returned to its former splendour – just go for it and enjoy the peace and contentment. Highly recommended.

| | |
|---|---|
| **Open:** *Closed Jan-Feb* | **Swimming Pool/Health Club:** *No* |
| **No. Rooms:** *7 Suites* | **Conference Facilities:** *No* |
| **Room telephones:** *Yes* | **Price Guide:** *Double £300.00 - £500.00 (all suites)* |
| **TV in Rooms:** *Yes* | *Seasonal breaks available* |
| **Pets:** *Yes*   **Children:** *Over 16* | **Location:** *Next to Inverewe Gardens.* |
| **Disabled**: *No* | |

*AA* 🏵 🏵
★★★

# CUILLIN HILLS HOTEL

Portree, Isle of Skye, Inverness-shire. IV51 9QU
Tel: 01478 612003   Fax: 01478 613092
Email: info@cuillinhills-hotel-skye.co.uk  www.cuillinhills-hotel-skye.co.uk

Built in the 1870s as a hunting lodge for Lord Macdonald of the Isles this hotel enjoys one of the finest and most spectacular views in Scotland overlooking Portree Bay and beyond. I have stayed here on numerous occasions (including Xmas) - the refurbishment programme over the years has added a new dimension to this hotel. Premier bedrooms offer that little bit of extra comfort - spacious and excellent en suite facilities with views over Portree harbour. Three 'courtyard' rooms (10 yards from main building) have all been fully upgraded to an executive status. Ever changing menus make good use of natural local produce including highland game, lobster, scallops and other fresh seafood. A fine dining experience here indeed - candle lit with views over the bay added to the enjoyment. Service could not be faulted. Other facilities include corporate hospitality - ideal for that board meeting and as one would expect weddings are very popular in the perfect location. The magnificent Cuillin Hills beckon. 2 AA rosetted restaurant. Also 'twinned' with Kincraig House Hotel on the A9 near Invergordon. (See entry under town name Inverness). Your host: Murray McPhee.

| | |
|---|---|
| **Open:** *All year* | **Swimming Pool/Health Club:** *No* |
| **No. Rooms:** *27 En Suite 27* | **Conference Facilities:** *Yes* |
| **Room telephones:** *Yes* | **Price Guide:** *Single £60.00-£80.00* |
| **TV in Rooms:** *Yes* | *Double £120.00-£230.00* |
| **Pets:** *No*  **Children:** *Yes* | **Location:** *Turn right ¼ mile north of Portree on A855 and* |
| **Disabled:** *Ground floor only* | *follow signs for hotel* |

*AA* ❀ ❀

*By kind permission of Eddrachilles Hotel*

# EDDRACHILLES HOTEL

Badcall Bay, Scourie, Sutherland. IV27 4TH
Tel: 01971 502080  Fax: 01971 502477
Email: enq@eddrachilles.com  www.eddrachilles.com

This hotel is superbly situated on Badcall Bay with magnificent views. This building was a former manse and has been completely refurbished providing every comfort. This is a mecca for wildlife enthusiasts with native otters, seals, roe and red deer. Handa Island nearby is a bird sanctuary and there are many small islands in the bay that can be visited by boat. The 11 ensuite bedrooms are comfortably furnished, some with views over the bay. Resident proprietors, Richard and Isabelle Flannery, demonstrate a commitment to the comfort of their guests with excellent home cooking and menus offering a varied choice. Good use of fresh natural Scottish produce locally sourced. A feature of the hotel is the sun porch which is tastefully furnished and where one can relax after dinner with coffee and liqueur. Excellent base for excursions to Durness and Cape Wrath in the north or Ullapool and The Summer Isles to the south. Excellent value for money.

| | |
|---|---|
| **Open:** *March-October* | **Swimming Pool/Health Club:** *No* |
| **No. Rooms:** *11 En Suite 11* | **Conference Facilities:** *No* |
| **Room telephones:** *Yes* | **Price Guide:** *Single £64.00-£67.00* |
| **TV in Rooms:** *Yes* | *Double £95.00-£120.00* |
| **Pets:** *No*  **Children:** *Any age* | **Location:** *Off A894 2 miles south of Scourie.* |
| **Disabled:** *Unsuitable* | *All rooms no smoking* |

TORAVAIG YACHT "SOLUS"

# TORAVAIG HOUSE

**Knock Bay, Sleat, Isle of Skye, Inverness-shire. IV44 8RE**
**Tel: 0845 055 1117 and 01471 833231**
Email: info@skyehotel.co.uk  www.skyehotel.co.uk

Anne Gracie & Captain Kenneth Gunn have performed a 'wee miracle' at Toravaig House in a relatively short time. The house and magnificent landscaped gardens are now complete (although I understand there are more plans to develop this property) and the views over to Knoydart are quite spectacular. Just add to this the luxury yacht SOLUS, (see opposite and for the exclusive use of hotel residents) in the responsible care of ship's master Kenneth, and you have what some would describe as the perfect retreat. I have monitored and stayed here each year – the bedrooms are furnished to an extremely high standard with all modern amenities including Sky satellite TV, CD player and telephone/modem. The kitchen brigade headed up by Peter Woods (known to me for many years) demonstrates great dedication – clear ambition here to achieve high standards. Both the dining room and lounge (with proper open fire) create an atmosphere of well being  - in fact, it is quite apparent on my visits here, that you just seem to relax without noticing it and enjoy the company, good food and a good night's sleep. Excellent hosts Anne and Kenneth have created a magnificent holiday retreat. (with quality) Not far from the Mallaig-Armsdale ferry with recent road improvement. Once here you will return...

| | |
|---|---|
| **Open:** *All year ex. 2wks Jan* | **Swimming Pool/Health Club:** *No* |
| **No. Rooms:** *9 En Suite 9* | **Conference Facilities:** *No* |
| **Room telephones:** *Yes* | **Price Guide:** *Single from £69.50* |
| **TV in Rooms:** *Yes (satellite)* | *Double £120.00-£150.00 per room* |
| **Pets:** *No*   **Children:** *No* | **Location:** *3mls from Armadale Ferry.* |
| **Disabled:** *Dining only* | *11mls from Broadford via Skye Bridge.* |

**AA**

# PARK LODGE HOTEL

### 32 Park Terrace, Stirling FK8 2JS
### Tel: 01786 474862  Fax: 01786 449748
Email: info@parklodge.net  www.parklodge.net

This is a fine Georgian mansion with walled garden situated in a delightful part of the town overlooking Stirling Castle. There are also fine views of the Campsie Fell hills and beyond. The furnishings are luxurious and reflect an era of gracious elegance. The bedrooms (some with 4 poster) are a delight – all en suite and again in the mould of a past era. The cuisine here is excellent - the culinary skills of French chef Georges Marquetty and his son Jean Pierre should be recognised but Georges is modest about his achievements but well known to his faithful followers. Anne Marquetty on hand to assure you of a warm welcome - known this family for seventeen years now and can thoroughly recommend a stay over in Stirling at this establishment. There is a well stocked cocktail bar with a wide range of malt whiskies – tempting in itself after a splendid meal. There is so much of Scotland's heritage here in Stirling to see and visit. The film 'Braveheart' highlighted the story of Sir William Wallace and the famous battle of Stirling Bridge in 1297.  Only 15 minutes walk to the centre of the town.

| | |
|---|---|
| **Open:** *All year* | **Swimming Pool/Health Club:** *No* |
| **No. Rooms:** *10 En Suite 10* | **Conference Facilities:** *Up to 50, functions up to 150* |
| **Room telephones:** *Yes* | **Price Guide:** *Single from £70.00 Double from £100.00* |
| **TV in Rooms:** *Yes* | *Suite: £150.00* |
| **Pets:** *Yes* **Children:** *Yes* | **Location:** *Opposite golf course in King's Park.* |
| **Disabled:** *Yes* | |

# BALINAKILL COUNTRY HOUSE HOTEL
By Tarbert, Argyll. PA29 6XL
Tel: 01880 740206   Fax: 01880 740298
Email: info@balinakill.com   www.balinakill.com

Neglected over the years Angus and Susan MacDiarmid have painstakingly renovated this beautiful Victorian B listed mansion house and it is being noticed. Secluded within its own 6 acres of woodland and garden with sweeping lawns you will find it just 10 miles south of Tarbert at the village of Clachan. In the atmosphere of a bygone era you will find every modern comfort – many of the orginal features of the house built in 1890 have been retained including ornate ceilings etc. Large bedrooms offer every comfort – some 4 poster for that special occasion. Many can provide the luxury of a log fire. The drawing room and sitting room (oak panelled) are massive with comfy furniture and also with log fires. Cuisine is wholesome and expertly prepared – Islay scallops, Ayrshire lamb or Tarbert cod could be your choice here at a very reasonable cost I should add. There are a host of outdoor pursuits – some arranged through the hotel. This is a lovely part of Argyll – ferry terminal closeby for Islay & Gigha and a short drive to Campbeltown. The work at Balinakill is ongoing but Angus and Susan have done a tremendous job to bring this property back from 'the brink'. Excellent value for money. VisitScotland 3 star hotel.

**Open:** *Closed November*
**No. Rooms:** *10 En Suite 10*
**Room telephones:** *No*
**TV in Rooms:** *Yes*
**Pets:** *Allocated*   **Children:** *Over 12*
**Disabled:** *Dining only*

**Swimming Pool/Health Club:** *No*
**Conference Facilities:** *Up to 20*
**Price Guide:** *Single £45.00*
*Double £80.00-£90.00 (seasonal breaks)*
**Location:** *10mls south of Tarbert (Loch Fyne) on A83 at village of Clachan.*

# STONEFIELD CASTLE HOTEL

Tarbert, Loch Fyne, Argyll. PA29 6YJ
Tel: 01880 820836  Fax: 01880 820929
(no email or website address available at time of going to press - contact by telephone only)

Stonefield Castle is set in 60 acres of woodland gardens that contain some of the finest Himalayan Rhododendrons and other exotic shrubs. The castle is a superb example of Scottish Baronial architecture built in 1837. It has retained much of its original furnishings, wood panelling, ornate ceilings and marble fireplaces alongside family portraits. Relax in the two spacious lounges or sample a pre-dinner drink in the panelled cocktail bar. Experience the very best of Scottish cuisine including shellfish, seasonal game and the famous Loch Fyne kipper. The view from the dining room over Loch Fyne is one of the best I have seen. Away from the 'hustle and bustle' there are corporate facilities here for up to 150 persons and weddings are popular in such a perfect setting. Very handy overnight stay for the Islay Ferry or stay awhile and explore this wonderful part of Argyll. Recreational activities include golf, horse riding, sea and loch fishing.

| | |
|---|---|
| **Open:** *All year* | **Swimming Pool/Health Club:** *No* |
| **No. Rooms:** *33 En Suite 33* | **Conference Facilities:** *Yes* |
| **Room telephones:** *Yes* | **Price Guide:** *Single £90.00–£100.00* |
| **TV in Rooms:** *Yes* | *Double £180.00–£250.00 (suites)* |
| **Pets:** *By arrangement*  **Children:** *Yes* | **Location:** *From Lochgilpead take Tarbert Road (A83)* |
| **Disabled:** *Limited* | *south for 10 miles.* |

**AA**

# FORSS HOUSE HOTEL

Forss, By Thurso, Caithness. KW14 7XY

Tel: 01847 861201  Fax: 01847 861301

Email: anne@forsshousehotel.co.uk  www.forsshousehotel.co.uk

Only 4 miles from Thurso on the A836 you will find Forss House Hotel nestling in 20 acres of woodland beside a picturesque water mill. The investment by the owners (also of the internationally renowned Ackergill Tower near Wick) over the last 2 years has been impressive. The 4 main bedrooms have all been refurbished to an extremely high standard. The professional input with the interior furnishings and fabrics are evident. Large en suite bathrooms are a delight – with that professional input so evident in the bedrooms. Again, the kitchen remains a priority with a dedicated team producing dishes of a sound quality, clarity of flavours using fresh local ingredients. The private dining room is ideal for that special occasion or corporate business meeting and is completely functional for most purposes. In the well maintained gardens there are 5 sportsmen's lodges – some of the best fishing in Scotland can be found in this area. The cocktail bar with 300 malts and log fire exudes peace and contentment. It's difficult to find a place of this quality in the 'far north' – there are more plans to develop this property even further with the comfort of the guest in mind. Only 15 minutes from the Castle of Mey (now open to the public). John O' Groats just "up the road" and convenient day trip to Orkney. Go for it…

| | |
|---|---|
| **Open:** *All year (closed 23rd Dec – 4th Jan)* | **Disabled:** *Limited* |
| **No. Rooms:** *13 En Suite 13* | **Swimming Pool/Health Club:** *No* |
| **Room telephones:** *Yes* | **Conference Facilities:** *Up to 30* |
| **TV in Rooms:** *Yes* | **Price Guide:** *Single from £70.00-£85.00* |
| **Pets:** *Yes* | *Double from £105.00-£135.00* |
| **Children:** *Yes* | **Location:** *4 miles from Thurso on A836* |

The King and I

# FARLAM HALL

Brampton, Cumbria. CA8 2NG

Tel: 016977 46234   Fax: 016977 46683

Email: farlam@relaischateaux.com   www.farlamhall.co.uk

This is truly a magnificent 17th century ivy clad country manor set amongst wonderful parkland and woodland policies – a member of the prestigious Relais & Chateaux no less. The lake and fountain to the front a remarkable feature – from the moment you arrive and enter Farlam Hall there is an atmosphere of peace and contentment. A stroll in the gardens with afternoon tea sets the tone – bedrooms are extremely comfortable – spacious (large windows) and well furnished complimented by large en suite bathrooms. The Quinion and Stevenson families have owned Farlam Hall since 1975 and the finest traditions of hotel keeping are evident. The comfort of the guest is paramount. Add to this the fine cuisine (2 AA rosettes) and attentive service and you have the complete product. Tartar of Wild Solway Salmon, fillet of Wild Sea Bass or Breast of Lancashire Guinea Fowl could be your choice with a daily changing menu. Home made desserts 'to die for'. Just 'over the border' this is an ideal stop whether travelling north or south. Hadrian's Wall and many other historical sites closeby. Go for it, indulge yourself. Enjoyed my stay here and will return. 3 AA red stars.

| | | |
|---|---|---|
| **Open:** *All year ex. 24th - 31st Dec* | **Swimming Pool/Health Club:** *No* | |
| **No. Rooms:** *12 En Suite 12* | **Conference Facilities:** *Up to 12 director level* | |
| **Room telephones:** *Yes* | **Price Guide:** *Single £150.00-£170.00* | |
| **TV in Rooms:** *Yes* | *Double £280.00-£320.00* | |
| **Pets:** *Yes*  **Children:** *Over 5* | **Location:** | *Junction 43 on M6. 12 miles on A689 to* |
| **Disabled:** *Not suitable* | | *Alston.* |

# MARLFIELD HOUSE

### Gorey, Co. Wexford, Ireland.
### Tel: (00353) 5394 21124   Fax: (00353) 5394 21572
Email: info@marlfieldhouse.ie   www.marlfieldhouse.com

Once again I am delighted to include Marlfield House as my Irish 'Associate Hotel' for edition 2007. It came strongly recommended and is a member of the prestigious Relais & Chateaux group. Formerly the residence of the Earls of Courtown Marlfield House is a very elegant 19th. century mansion set in its own grounds of wonderful garden, woodland and parkland policies. The State Rooms are decorated with rich fabrics and fine antique furniture - all have period marble fireplaces and elegant marble bathrooms. Every room is spacious and offers every luxury. The interior of the hotel is resplendent with fine paintings and antiques and the conservatory is a feature overlooking the garden. Modern Irish cuisine here which has been awarded 3 AA red rosettes for food. The Bowe family are to be congratulated on keeping the standards of yesterday today. To maintain such high standards is testament to a firm commitment and dedication. Relais & Chateaux member since 1984. 3 AA red stars, 3 AA red rosettes (food). General Manager: Margaret Bowe.

| | |
|---|---|
| **Open:** *Feruary - mid December* | **Swimming Pool/Health Club:** *No* |
| **No. Rooms:** *13 (6 suites) En Suite 13* | **Conference Facilities:** *Small - Director Level* |
| **Room telephones:** *Yes* | **Price Guide:** *Double. Room - Standard:* **Euro 230-445** |
| **TV in Rooms:** *Yes* | *State Rooms:* **Euro 490-765 (Master)** |
| **Pets:** *Arrangement*   **Children:** *Yes* | **Location:** *80 km south of Dublin* |
| **Disabled:** *Not suitable* | |

*AA*✿✿✿
★★★

# STEVENSONS

## SCOTLAND'S
## GOOD FOOD BOOK WITH RECIPES
## 2007

Photo by kind permission of The Seafood Restaurant, St. Andrews

# STEVENSONS

## SCOTLAND'S
## GOOD FOOD BOOK
## 2007

# FOREWORD

*I have seen many major changes during my 20 years in the hospitality industry; some I welcome and some I don't. The smoking ban has now been implemented in Scotland; I haven't seen any impact on the restaurant industry as yet and welcome the government's strong stance on this.*

*On the other hand, both of my restaurants are fortunate to have fantastic locations overlooking the Firth of Forth and the North Sea, and while most of our fish now comes down from Aberdeen, our lobsters are still very much local, so local in fact that my customers can see them being caught from their table. Now, the government wants these very same lobsters to be transported from the harbour in St Monans down to London to a centralized and regulated market, and then back up to my kitchen beside the harbour in St Monans. We chefs are all trying hard to promote the use of fresh local produce in our restaurants and support our local suppliers, but the idea of sending fresh shellfish on a 2 day return journey seems ill-thought out and contrary to the very foundations of good catering practice; it is also harmful to the environment.*

*The second initiative introduced by the government this year is 'Cooksafe'. We are required now to record at what time the lobsters were caught, by whom, what temperature were they during the round trip St Monans-London-St Monans, who packed them, who signed for them, who checked the use-by date (does a live lobster have one and where is it? Answers on a postcard, please.) and what temperature did the lobster reach during cooking? With having two restaurants and a deli, this takes up valuable time away from the stove, filling in the endless paperwork. The reason behind this initiative is to regulate the catering industry and to prevent or reduce the number of food poisonings. The point that the government is failing to grasp is that by making this industry more and more sterile, we are becoming more and more susceptible to bacteria, tummy illnesses and allergens.*

*Having said all that, it has been another good year in both restaurants. We are now into our 4th year in St Andrews, and our 14th in St Monans, and still as busy as ever. With such high standards and perseverance, Alan Stevenson has created an important guide for our industry in Scotland and it is a delight to be associated with him.*

*Craig Millar - Chef/ Director*

Craig Millar - Head Chef
*The Seafood Restaurant, St. Andrews*
*(3 AA Rosettes)*

# Scottish quality salmon

Quality Approved
SCOTTISH
SALMON

*Naturally they're the best*

www.scottishsalmon.co.uk

# FARLEYER & BEYOND (RESTAURANT & ROOMS)

Aberfeldy, Perthshire. PH15 2JE
Tel/Fax: 01887 820332
Email: delcaso@hotmail.co.uk  www.farleyer&beyond.com

There is a new kid 'on the block' here at Farleyer (Delcasso Ltd) and the whole dining experience was well worth the visit. Farleyer restaurant with rooms is located in a magnificent garden setting near Weem just outside Aberfeldy. The gifted duo of chef proprietor Callum Keir and his French wife Delphine (also pastry chef) have firmly set out their stall – menus are extremely well balanced with some really good combinations – not too long which facilitates the excellent use of fresh/seasonal produce (no doubt about it). I switched between lunch and dinner menus – quail starter (fantastic) lamb (perfection) and "Summer in a Glass" (berries, sorbet & ice cream) was to die for – Farleyer & Beyond as it is now called will do extremely well – culinary skills quite obvious and well executed. Spacious and comfortable table settings. Also don't forget the 3 comfortable rooms – all en suite. Further accolades to follow no doubt. Reserve your table now! A wonderful culinary experience.

| | | | |
|---|---|---|---|
| **Open:** *All year* | | **Covers:** | *34* |
| **No Rooms:** *3 en suite* | | **Price Guide:** | *DBB £72.00 - £91.00* |
| **TV in Rooms:** *Yes* | | | *Dinner: £28.50 - £33.00   Lunch: £6.95 - £25.00* |
| **Room Tel.** *Yes* | | **Location:** | *Aberfeldy. Over bridge to Castle Menzies -* |
| **Children:** *Yes* | **Disabled:** *Dining* | | *1ml after castle on right (rear entrance)* |

# ANDREW FAIRLIE@GLENEAGLES

The Gleneagles Hotel, Auchterarder, Perthshire. PH3 1NF
Tel: 01764 694267  Fax: 01764 694163.
Email: andrew.fairlie@gleneagles.com

Known by reputation Andrew displays a passion for food and is driven by innovation, evolving ideas and concepts, with an element of excitement and daring. Sourced every year, technical skills are obvious in traditional or modern dishes with a consistency throughout - accurate and vibrant flavours. The importance of team work is vital states Andrew - he moved his team from Glasgow and Dale Dewsbury (General Manager) works miracles with the front of house operation. Ambience and service could not be faulted. Sophisticated wine list. Options of a la carte or tasting menu. Excellent cheese board. This is one for the connoisseur - the complete dining experience. **2 Michelin Stars, AA UK Chefs chef of the year 2006-2007, Scottish chef of the year 2002. AA restaurant of the year 2002 - Scotland & Northern Ireland. AA**🏵🏵🏵🏵 🍴

| | | |
|---|---|---|
| **Open:** *All year (Dinner only) ex 3wks Jan. Closed Sun.* | **Disabled:** *Unsuitable* | |
| **No Rooms:** *N/A* | **Covers:** | *40* |
| **TV in Rooms:** *N/A* | **Price Guide:** | *£60.00 - £80.00* |
| **Room Tel.** *N/A* | | *Cheese £12.00 Coffee £5.00* |
| **Children:** *Over 12* | **Location:** | *Ground floor of Gleneagles Hotel.* |

# CULTER MILL RESTAURANT

**Coulter Village, Biggar. ML12 6PZ**

Tel/Fax: 01899 220950

Email: cultermill@hotmail.co.uk  www.cultermill.co.uk

Driving down the A702 through Biggar to Abington (or visa versa) slow down and nip into this restaurant (lunch & dinner) and you will experience a real culinary triumph. With a chequered history, which made me bypass this establishment over the years, it has now been acquired by chef/proprietor Ashley Gallant and his partner Clair. His cuisine has been sourced by me for several years, previously with a country house hotel. A fine dining experience here – Ashley's philosophy is that all produce must be fresh and where possible bought locally – hence menus change with the seasons. Merited with 2 AA red rosttes for a number of years Ashley has won numerous other accolades. His burning ambition is to utilise his freedom and raise standards even higher – flair and imagintion come through with great technique and balance. The venue of the old rustic mill (ample car parking at rear) creates the perfect ambience. Just slow down a bit at the bridge and sample the fayre. Highly recommended.

| | | | |
|---|---|---|---|
| **Open:** *All yr. Except Oct-Apr open Wed-Sat.* | | **Disabled:** | *Yes* |
| *Sun 12.30-9pm* | | **Covers:** | *45 (comfortably)* |
| **No Rooms:** *N/A* | | **Price Guide:** | *Lunch: £7.50 - £25.00* |
| **TV in Rooms:** *N/A* | **Room Tel.** *N/A* | | *Dinner: £12.50 - £30.00* |
| **Children:** *Yes* | | **Location:** | *Village of Culter 1 mile south of Biggar.* |

# DUCK'S AT LE MARCHÉ NOIR

**14 Eyre Place, Edinburgh. EH3 5EP**

Tel: 0131 558 1608  Fax: 0131 556 0798

Email: enquiries@ducks.co.uk  www.ducks.co.uk

Well known intimate restaurant on the north side of Edinburgh and visited on occasions by Sean Connery & Princess Anne. (Name dropping again!!) This well established restaurant is renowned for its consistency and its very fine and extensive wine list. Candlelit dinners provide a terrific ambience. A la carte menus provide a range of dishes expertly cooked – mainly traditional but with some innovation. A dedication and passion within the kitchen to maintain high standards – quality sourced suppliers combined with good techniques produce the perfect meal. Service and attention to detail were exemplary. Crisp white linen and fine glassware add to your enjoyment. Fish, meat, seafood, vegetarian or just traditional haggis could be one of your choices. There are ornamental ducks all over the place here as befits the name of this establishment - certainly has a corporate identity!!! Not far from Princes Street this comes well recommended. Your host: Malcolm Duck.

| | | |
|---|---|---|
| **Open:** *Closed Christmas & Boxing Days* | **Disabled:** | *Not suitable* |
| **No Rooms:** *N/A* | **Covers:** | *50* |
| **TV in Rooms:** *N/A* | **Price Guide:** | *Lunch £12.00-£32.00 (a la carte)* |
| **Room Tel.** *N/A* | | *Dinner £15.00-£37.50 (a la carte)* |
| **Children:** *Yes* | **Location:** | *New Town near city centre* |

# HALDANES RESTAURANT

### 13B Dundas Street, Edinburgh. EH3 6QG
Tel: 0131 556 8407 and 0131 556 5707
Email: dinehaldanes@aol.com  www.haldanesrestaurant.com

Haldanes has moved 'round the corner' to Dundas Street and thankfully still down the hill from 'Harvey Nicks'! A basement restaurant once again Haldanes has continued its reputation as a leading player in Edinburgh – reviews have been exemplary. George Kelso (chef proprietor) and his wife Michelle (front of house) perform wonders - cuisine of the highest order – George produces dishes, mainly Scottish traditional, that would tempt anyone. He works miracles with locally sourced fresh produce (some innovation as well) and displays great culinary skills. Clear well defined flavours and a consistency throughout the meal. There is a designated wine bar here - also very popular private dining facilities. With a first class wine list to complement a fine meal combined with great ambience this is a culinary triumph not to be missed. 2 AA red rosette award. Member of The Scotch Beef Club. Reservations advised. **AA**🏵🏵

| | | | |
|---|---|---|---|
| **Open:** *All year ex. 25th/26th Dec.* | **Disabled:** | *Unsuitable* | |
| **No Rooms:** *N/A* | **Covers:** | *34 comfortably* | |
| **TV in Rooms:** *N/A* | **Price Guide:** | *Lunch from £15.00 (2 course)* | |
| **Room Tel.** *N/A* | | *Dinner £28.50-£45.00* | |
| **Children:** *Yes (well behaved!)* | **Location:** | *New Town - 100 yds from intersection with* | |
| | | *Hanover Street/Abercromby Place (same side).* | |

# NUMBER ONE RESTAURANT

### 1, Princes Street, Edinburgh. EH2 2EQ
Tel : 0131 557 6727   Fax : 0131 557 3747
Email : numberone@thebalmoralhotel.com  www.roccofortehotels.com

In keeping with the fine traditions of The Good Food Book this restaurant rightfully takes its place amongst the others included in my personal choice. Although part of The Balmoral Hotel the restaurant has created a reputation in its own right for fine dining - executive chef Jeff Bland whose culinary expertise is well known displays a quality of skills which have brought him recognition from many agencies and a number of awards. Jeff is equally at home with modern or traditional dishes - good combinations showing flair and imagination. High technical skills with some innovation, good texture and taste. There is a depth to the cusine here which is apparent throughout the meal. There can be no doubt that diners' expectations are fully realised - also a fine wine list available for the connoisseur. Ambience perfect with fine furnishings and white linen - sound advice and service impeccable. **Michelin Star**. Restaurant Manager: Gary Quinn. **AA**🏵 🏵 🏵

| | | | |
|---|---|---|---|
| **Open:** *Closed first 2 weeks January* | **Children:** | *Yes* **Disabled:** | *Access available* |
| *Sun-Thurs: 19.00 - 22.00* | **Covers:** | *50* | |
| *Thurs + Fri: 19.00 - 22.30* | **Price Guide:** | *Dinner from £48.00 per person* | |
| **No Rooms:** *188 (five star facilities)* | | *(excluding wine)* | |
| **TV in Rooms:** *N/A* **Room Tel.** *N/A* | **Location:** | *East end of Princes Street* | |

# THE BUTTERY

**652 Argyle Street, Glasgow. G3 8UF**
Tel: 0141 221 8188   Fax: 0141 204 4639
Email: ia.fleming@btopenworld.com

Established in 1869, this is Glasgow's oldest and most celebrated restaurant. Stained glass doors lead you past the impressive mahogany and marble bar into the unique wood-panelled dining room. Owner Ian Fleming and Executive Chef Christopher Watson form a formidable team renowned for their management and culinary skills. The decor has been 'toned down' a bit from the Victorian image but still retains the elegance it always had - table settings perfect with crisp linen and sparkling cutlery. Front of house skills are obvious and the quality of food was consistent throughout the meal. Christopher's motto of "taste is the key" with flavour and presentation has always been his trademark and he brings the best out of good basic ingredients. **AA Restaurant of the Year (2003-04) Scotland and Northern Ireland**. True testament to a first class operation.

| | | | |
|---|---|---|---|
| **Open:** *Closed Sun/Mon, Sat lunch.* | | **Covers:** | *50* |
| *Xmas Day.* | | **Price Guide:** | *Lunch from £12.00-£25.00* |
| **No Rooms:** *N/A* | | | *Dinner £34.00-£38.00* |
| **Children:** *Yes* | | **Location:** | *Turn left at mini r/about at end of Elderslie Street* |
| **Disabled:** *Dining on ground level.* | | | *On left in Argyle Street.* |

# LA BONNE AUBERGE

**161 West Nile Street, Glasgow. G1 2RL**
Tel: 0141 352 8310   Fax: 0141 332 7447
Email: contactus@labonneauberge.com   www.labonneauberge.co.uk

This was the original Brasserie opened in 1975 by hotelier and restaurateur Maurice Taylor and today it still forms an integral part of the city's exceptional restaurant scene. The ethos behind this project was the brasserie concept in its purest form. This is quality French Mediterranean cuisine served in comfortable and relaxed surroundings. This restaurant, although part of the Holiday Inn Theatreland, stands on its own merit and the a la carte menu is a must - head chef Gerry Sharkey demonstrates good technical skills - simple but uncomplicated dishes with a certain amount of innovation and a french influence. Casual dining or an excellent table d'hôte menu (2 or 3 course) available with good choice of wines. Private dining can be arranged (exclusive use) in the Mont Marte suite - ideally placed for the The Royal Concert Hall nearby. 1 AA red rosette for food. Restaurant Manager Sean Simpson. **AA** ❀

| | | | |
|---|---|---|---|
| **Open:** *All year* | | **Disabled:** | *Yes* |
| **No Rooms:** *N/A* | | **Covers:** | *110* |
| **TV in Rooms:** *N/A* | | **Price Guide:** *Lunch: £6.95 - £12.95* | |
| **Room Tel.** *N/A* | | | *Dinner: £12.95 - £25.00 (pre theatre)* |
| **Children:** *Yes* | | **Location:** | *Opposite Royal Concert Hall.* |

# STRAVAIGIN

### 28 Gibson Street, Hillhead, Glasgow. G12 8NX
Tel: 0141 334 2665   Fax: 0141 334 4099.
Email: bookings@stravaigin.com   www.stravaigin.com

This restaurant and cafe bar is the domain of Colin Clydesdale - a name synonymous with food in Glasgow. Situated in the busy west end of Glasgow the restaurant occupies the basement beneath the cafe bar - this provides the option of a more comprehensive menu or a quick meal in the cafe bar. The bistro type atmosphere is prevalent throughout - informality with genuine Glasgow hospitality. Your choice could include seared scallops, roast oriental duck with a soba noodle strudel and mango coriander jus - to finish a chocolate cherry bread pudding with white pepper ice-cream and cherry compote. Ever changing menus and options are available - Colin uses his culinary skills to introduce new dishes with great success - this is reflected in the 2 AA red rosettes awarded to this establishment and Stravaigin was voted best restaurant of the year in 1998 by The Scottish Chefs Association. *AA*⊛⊛

| | |
|---|---|
| **Open:** *All year ex. 25/26/31st Dec. Jan 1st. Sun Lunch* | **Disabled:** *Unsuitable* |
| **No Rooms:** *N/A* | **Covers:** *76* |
| **TV in Rooms:** *N/A* | **Price Guide:** *Dinner: 2 courses £22.95  3 courses £27.95* |
| **Room Tel.** *N/A* | *Lunch: from £12.95* |
| **Children:** *Yes* | **Location:** *M8, junct 17 or A82 from city centre - Gt Western road, turn down park road, rt into Gibson St., 200 yds on right* |

# CRAGGAN MILL RESTAURANT & GALLERY

### By Grantown-On-Spey, Morayshire. PH26 3NT
Tel : 01479 872288   Fax : 01479 872288
Email : info@cragganmill.co.uk   www.cragganmill.co.uk

Graham Harvey & Sheila McConachie (Associate Master Chef of Great Britain) are forging ahead here and have established themselves as a popular food destination in this scenic area of Strathspey just outside Grantown-on-Spey. Attractive garden setting (ample parking) with real country atmosphere you will not be disappointed with Sheila's culinary expertise – renowned for their signature dish of fresh mussels with a choice of 7 sauces they have introduced a new signature dish of scallops with some interesting combinations. Menus offer quite a varied choice – evidence of innovation which clearly demonstrates Sheila's dedication and sound technical skills. Good use of seasonal fresh produce from quality suppliers. Home made bread, ice cream and sorbets as well as canapés before dinner. Recipient of numerous awards this restaurant was recently awarded 2 AA food rosettes. Always creating rather than following others a visit here is mandatory and should be included on your itinerary. *AA*⊛ ⊛

| | | |
|---|---|---|
| **Open:** *All year except Tuesdays* | **Covers:** | *50* |
| **No Rooms:** *N/A* | **Price Guide:** | *Lunch £7.50-£15.00* |
| **TV in Rooms:** *N/A*  **Room Tel.** *N/A* | | *Dinner £15.00-£30.00 (3 courses)* |
| **Children:** *Yes* | **Location:** | *Outskirts of Grantown en route to Aviemore.* |
| **Disabled:** *Category 3 (VisitScotland)* | | *Right hand side leaving Grantown - half mile.* |

# ABSTRACT RESTAURANT

20 Ness Bank, Inverness. IV2 4SF
Tel: 01463 223777  Fax: 01463 712378
Email: reception@glenmoristontownhouse.com  www.abstractrestaurant.com

An integral part of The Glenmoriston Town House this restaurant ranks as one of the finest in Scotland. Apart from the publicity generated by the visit of celebrity chef Gordon Ramsay this should be on your itinery, whether a 'foodie' or not – an experience not to be missed. Head chef Loic Lefebvre and kitchen brigade display great dedication – high technical skills are obvious with ambition to create high standards and be consistent throughout all phases of the meal. Despite the comments of our 'peers', I visit here regularly – combinations are quite exciting and different. No 'restricted' menu here – excellent choice of meat and fish dishes or the 7 course tasting menu. Foie gras ravioli, red mullet, quail salad, lobster, spring Scottish lamb and Barbary duck just part of this choice. Flavour exemplary and expectations are fully met. The chef's table in the kitchen is innovation itself – great ambience with knowledgeable and attentive staff. A terrific wine list to boot. Ample car parking. *AA* 🏵 🏵

| | | | |
|---|---|---|---|
| **Open:** *All year* | | **Covers:** | *35* |
| **No Rooms:** *30* | | **Price Guide:** *Lunch from £14.00* | |
| **TV in Rooms:** *Yes* | **Room Tel.** *Yes* | *Dinner from £34.00* | |
| **Children:** *Yes* | | *Tasting Menu from £50.00* | |
| **Disabled:** *Yes* | | **Location:** *Ness Bank 5 minutes from CityCentre* | |

# THE GROUSE AND CLARET RESTAURANT

Heatheryford, Kinross. KY13 ONQ
Tel: 01577 864212  Fax: 01577 864920
Email: grouseandclaret@lineone.net  www.grouseandclaret.net

The Grouse and Claret is really a country centre which combines accommodation, an art gallery and a fishery. It is very conveniently situated just off the M90 between Edinburgh and Perth in a rural setting - in fact there are 25 acres encompassing restaurant, art gallery, fishery and meadow. Over the last number of years chef/proprietor David Futong and his wife Vicki have earned an enviable reputation for quality cuisine in an ideal setting. The conservatory adds a new dimension - spacious dining area with views over the meadow. Menus are sensible and cater for all tastes - great emphasis on delicious home made food, beautifully presented - seasonal game and fresh shell fish including lobster and crayfish a house speciality. This is a wonderful setting for small weddings and functions. Comfortable detached bedrooms - some overlooking the trout ponds make this the ideal base in the country only a short drive from the city hazards of Edinburgh. Ample car parking.

| | | | |
|---|---|---|---|
| **Open:** *All year ex. 2 wks. end of Jan.Sun.night/Mon* | **Disabled:** *Yes* | **Covers:** | *60* |
| **No Rooms:** *3  En Suite 3* | **Price Guide:** *Double B&B £75.00. Single B&B £50.00* | | |
| **TV in Rooms:** *Yes* | *Lunch £10.50-£16.50* | | |
| **Room Tel.** *No* | *Dinner £18.00-£25.00 (à la carte)* | | |
| **Children:** *Yes* | **Location:** *Leave M90 Junction (6) then 500 yds - Private Road Opposite Service Station* | | |

# LIVINGSTON'S RESTAURANT
### 52 High Street, Linlithgow, West Lothian. EH49 7AE
Tel: 01506 846565  Fax: 01506 846565
Email: contact@livingstons-restaurant.co.uk  www.livingstons-restaurant.co.uk

This charming restaurant in Linlithgow has built up an enviable reputation and has consistently held the 2 AA rosette award - an indication in itself of the high quality of cuisine maintained. The charm is in the form of a 'cottage' reached through a vennel off the main street which opens up into a wonderful garden setting. A family business there is emphasis of a personal note here coupled with excellent front of house service. Food prepared demonstrates excellent combinations and balance of ingredients with a consistency throughout all courses. Menus offer a mixture of signature and other innovative choices. Meals include Christine Livingston's legendary tablet and coffee. A very relaxed atmosphere here - previous winner of Scotland's 'out of town' restaurant. Excellent wine list. Hosts: Ronald, Christine & Derek Livingston. *AA* 🏵 🏵

| | | | |
|---|---|---|---|
| **Open:** *Closed Sun/Mon & 1st 2 weeks Jan and 1 week June & Oct* | **Children:** | *Over 8 (evening)* | |
| | **Disabled:** | *Yes* | |
| **No Rooms:** *N/A* | **Covers:** | *50* | |
| **TV in Rooms:** *N/A* | **Price Guide:** *Lunch £13.50-£16.50 Dinner £27.00-£32.50* | | |
| **Room Tel.** *N/A* | **Location:** *Eastern end of High Street opp. Post Office.* | | |

# CREEL RESTAURANT WITH ROOMS
### Front Road, St. Margaret's Hope, Orkney. KW17 2SL
Tel: 01856 831311
Email: alan@thecreel.freeserve.co.uk  www.thecreel.co.uk

Although not quite on your doorstep this is a mecca for all who enjoy food prepared to consistently high standards on the south part of Orkney just over the Churchill Barriers and 14 miles from Kirkwall. Spent 2 nights with Alan and Joyce Craigie taking the Gillsbay Ferry directly into St. Margaret's Hope and a short drive to the 'restaurant with rooms'. Alternatively there is a ferry from Scrabster. There is complete dedication here - food prepared using much of the island produce but with originality, flair and imagination that reflect a high quality of culinary skills. It could be described as modern cooking with a hint of Orcadian influence. The Creel has 2 AA red rosettes and is rated highly in the Good Food Guide (UK). A bit of an adventure getting there but an experience not to be missed. *AA* 🏵 🏵 🏆

| | | | |
|---|---|---|---|
| **Open:** *Closed Jan/Feb. Open Apr-Sept & weekends Nov/Dec* | **Disabled:** | *Unsuitable* | |
| | **Covers:** | *34* | |
| **No Rooms:** *3 En Suite* | **Price Guide:** *B/B single from £65.00* | | |
| **TV in Rooms:** *Yes*  **Room Tel.** *No* | *B/B double from £95.00* | | |
| | *Dinner: from £34.00* | | |
| **Children:** *Over 5* | **Location:** *A961 South across Churchill barriers. 20 mins from Kirkwall* | | |

# DEANS AT LET'S EAT

**77-79 Kinnoull Street, Perth. PH1 5EZ**
Tel: 01738 643377   Fax: 01738 621464
Email: deans@letseatperth.co.uk   www.letseatperth.co.uk

Willie Deans has wasted no time in marking his card in Perth – assessment and incoming reports indicate that he has raised standards even higher. His distinguished career is well documented and he and his wife Margo now operate this very successful restaurant in Perth. The foundation of this success has been a lot of hard work, not only in the kitchen, but the smooth operation at front of house. Great combinations here, whether fish, game, beef, or a rib eye from the grill. Ochil poultry (free range) or saddle of lamb a firm favourite. Even the chef's home made soup from the board menu always with just that something different. Quality ancillaries (bread, garnishes etc). Flair and imagination evident throughout the complete meal – culinary skills successfully executed and diners expectations fully met. One of the best areas (Fife not far away is another) to source quality fresh ingredients – even pick your own chanterelles & ceps! Highly recommended. – reservations for lunch/dinner advised. *AA* 🏵 🏵 🐖

| | | | |
|---|---|---|---|
| **Open:** *All year except Sun/Mon* | | **Disabled:** | *Yes* |
| **No Rooms:** *N/A*   **En suite:** *N/A* | | **Covers:** | *60* |
| **TV in Rooms:** *N/A* | | **Price Guide:** | *Lunch from £14.00* |
| **Room Tel.** *N/A* | | | *Dinner from £25.00* |
| **Children:** *Yes* | | **Location:** | *Corner Kinnoull/Atholl Street near North Inch.* |

# THE SEAFOOD RESTAURANT

**The Scores, St. Andrews, Fife. KY16 9AS**   Tel: 01334 479475   Fax: 01334 479476
**also at 16, West End, St. Monan's, Fife. KY10 2BX**   Tel: 01333 730327   Fax: 01333 730508
Email: info@theseafoodrestaurant.com   www.theseafoodrestaurant.com

Having sourced both restaurants this is a dining experience you will not forget – you are already making plans to revisit as you leave. The new premises at St. Andrews, all glass encased, is a wonder of modern architecture not far from the famous 18th green behind the club house. Both premises have stunning views to the sea – the interior design is fantastic (no expense spared). If you are into seafood, experience the culinary skills of co-owner/head-chef Craig Millar known to me for many years. Kilbrandon oysters, pan-seared collops of monkfish & lemon thyme panacotta was my choice last time – cooked to perfection. Fresh ingredients to compliment each dish – some innovation here with vibrant flavours. Perfect ambience and a total commitment by staff under the personal supervison of co-owner Tim Butler. A must for the connoisseur. **AA restaurant of the year - Scotland and Northern Ireland** (2004-2005). 3 AA red rosette award. See Food Forward. *AA* 🏵 🏵 🏵

| | | | |
|---|---|---|---|
| **Open:** *All year* | | **Covers:** | *60* |
| **No Rooms:** *N/A* | | **Price Guide:** | *Lunch £20.00-£24.00* |
| **TV in Rooms:** *N/A* | **Room Tel.** *N/A* | | *Dinner £35.00-£40.00* |
| **Children:** *Yes* | | **Location:** | *Pitching distance from R&A Clubhouse,* |
| **Disabled:** *Yes* | | | *below the Scores* |

# CREAGAN HOUSE WITH ACCOMMODATION

### Strathyre, Perthshire. FK18 8ND
Tel: 01877 384638   Fax: 01877 384319
Email: eatandstay@creaganhouse.co.uk   www.creaganhouse.co.uk

In the heart of Rob Roy country Creagan House was originally a farmhouse dating from the 17th. century but now restored and upgraded to provide a 'baronial' dining hall and 5 charming bedrooms - one a four poster. Strathyre, which means 'sheltered valley', is a village north of Callander and south of Balquhidder - it nestles at the head of Loch Lubnaig in marvellous surroundings which, I believe, inspired Sir Walter Scott. Proprietors Gordon & Cherry Gunn create a real homely atmosphere. I have known the Gunn family since 1990 and I can assure you of a warm welcome, excellent cuisine and very comfortable accommodation. Gordon is meticulous with his preparation and presentation. Using much of the local attributes of a rich arable Perthshire the menus include Gaelic fillet steak, fillet of venison, poached turbot with wonderful sauces and an excellent selection of seasonal vegetables. Home made desserts or Scottish cheeses are favourites. The dining room is an experience in itself and although non-residents are welcome Gordon & Cherry restrict the numbers of diners in order to maintain standards. AA 2 red rosettes for food and a member of The Scotch Beef Club. *AA* 🌺🌺 ★ 🐷

| | | | |
|---|---|---|---|
| **Open:** All year ex. Feb & 2 weeks Nov | **Disabled:** | Yes | |
| **No Rooms:** 5 En Suite | **Covers:** | 15 Parties 35 | |
| **TV in Rooms:** Yes | **Price Guide:** | DB&B £83.50 | |
| **Room Tel.** No | | B&B £55.00 (Rest closed Thurs eve) | |
| **Children:** Yes | **Location:** | Just north of Strathyre village between Callander & Lochearnhead | |

# RESTAURANT MICHAEL DEANE

### 36-40 Howard Street, Belfast. BT1 6PF
Tel: 02890 560000   Fax: 02890 560001
Email: info@michaeldeane.co.uk   www.michaeldeane.co.uk

Because this entry is from Belfast (associate restaurant) it causes quite an interest. I was fortunate to meet Michael Deane when he worked in the north of Scotland some years ago and sample his skills. At this stage his talents were not well known but it came as no surprise to hear of his reputation back in his native Belfast - he had opened his own establishment in 1997. His exhuberant style - both of showmanship and of uncompromisingly perfectionist cooking has elicited praise from the sternest of food critics and the most demanding food guides. Reluctant to classify his food - there are perceptible French, Pacific Rim, British and Irish influences in a typical menu - Michael Deane believes that it is the chef's imperative to set trends, rather than follow them. The secret is never to cease to innovate. From his beginnings at Claridges Michael has been on a pilgrimage - always propelled by his pure passion for food and its possibilities. **Michelin Star** and AA 4 red rosettes. UK Good Food Guide. Keep this one in mind and follow this entry whenever in Belfast. *AA* 🌺🌺🌺🌺

| | | | |
|---|---|---|---|
| **Open:** Closed Sun.-Tues. | **Disabled:** | Brasserie only | |
| **No Rooms:** N/A | **Covers:** | 35 | |
| **TV in Rooms:** N/A   **Room Tel.** N/A | **Price Guide:** Dinner: £45.00 (2 courses)- £62.00 | | |
| **Children:** Welcome | | Lunch: Brasserie - from £15.95 | |

# Cruden Bay Lobster with Seared Lochinver Scallops and a Tortellini of Lobster

## Ingredients:

1kg Lobster
3 Small Scallops
125g Lemon Sole Fillets
50g Diced Lobster Meal
100ml Double Cream
1 Whole Cepe Mushroom
1kg Strong Flour
8 Whole Eggs
10 Egg Yolks
Tsp Olive Oil
Sprig of Dill
250ml Fish Stock
Lobster Shells
Brandy
250ml Cream
50g Onions, 50g Celery,
50g Carrots, 50g White of Leek
Tbsp Tomato Puree
1 Whole Large Carrot
3 Asparagus Spears
125g Creamed Potatoes
25g Butter
Sprig of Flat Leaf Parsley

## Method:

Steam the 1kg lobster for 10 minutes or place in a boiling vinegar court bouillon for 25 minutes approximately. Refresh in iced cold water and when cold split in half and crack claws.

To make the Pasta:- 1kg strong white flour, 8 whole eggs, 10 egg yolks, seasoning, 1 tsp olive oil. Sieve flour and salt into a bowl. Make a well in the middle, add eggs and mix together with a fork. Knead until it becomes elasticated, cover with cling film and leave to rest in the fridge for 10 minutes.

Peel the potatoes and cook in salted water. Pass through a sieve when cooked and add butter and a little cream. Keep warm.
Peel asparagus and cook in salted water, then refresh. Peel carrots and cut into 6cm battons. Cook in salted water and refresh.

To make the Lobster Butter Sauce:- Fish stock, lobster shells, brandy, cream, onions, celery, carrots, leek, tomato puree. Sweat off vegetables, add tomato puree, brandy and flame. Add fish stock, then reduce by half. Break down shells, add cream and reduce again. Check seasoning and pass through a fine sieve. Place back in a clean pan and keep on side of stove.

To make the Lobster Mousseline:- 125g lemon sole , 50g lobster meat (diced), 100ml double cream, 1 egg, white salt and pepper, chopped dill. Place white fish in food processor with egg white, salt and pepper. Mix on high speed until smooth, add the cream slowly. Pass through a fine sieve and place in a bowl over ice and fold in remainder of cream, chives and diced lobster.

Roll out pasta with the use of a pasta machine. Cut into circles and egg wash edges. Place a little of the mousseline in the centre and fold over. Press down the edges and bring the corners together. Cook in boiling, salted water with a little oil. Place lobster under the grill with a little butter and seasoning to warm. Saute the scallops and sliced cepes in a hot pan until they take on some colour. Set aside and keep warm.

### To Serve:

Place a small quenelle of potato on the centre of each plate with the vegetables, scallops and tortellini around the potato. Sit the warmed lobster on top of the potato. Drizzle a little sauce round the plate. Garnish with a sprig of parsley.

*Executive Chef: Mike Stoddart*
**Marcliffe Hotel, Spa and Restaurant, Aberdeen. AB15 9YA**
(also see entry page 11)

# Raclette Tarte Fine

### Part 1: Preparation of Cheese (1 week in advance)

1 Camembert Lait cru
1 Perigeux truffle
White truffle oil

Cut the camembert through the middle lengthways with a hot knife making sure to cut straight. Slice the truffle thinly with a mandolin and place on one half of the cheese making a full circle and covering all the cheese. You should get three camemberts done with one 4oz truffle. Using a plastic bottle drizzle on some truffle oil and rub over the truffle, season and place on the other half of the cheese. Wrap in cling film tightly and place back in the wooden box. This must be put in the cheese fridge for at least a week before using.

### Part 2: Confit Onions

3 Onions
250g Unsalted butter
Bay leave, thyme, black peppercorns

Slice the onions finely and place into a medium sized pan with the melted butter. Tie the rest of the ingredients in a piece of muslin cloth and add to the pan. The onions should cooked over a low heat, making sure you stir the pan regulary so it doesn`t catch on the base of the pan, until they are soft. You may need to add 100ml of water to the pan to stop the butter from colouring. The onions must not be coloured.

### Part 3: Tarte Fine

Take one sheet of frozen puff pastry and cut out circles using the cutter which is third from largest in the set. Layer these between greaseproof and they can be stored in the freezer. Each service take out the required amount of discs and let them defrost on your bench which should be lightly floured. Using a rolling pin carefully roll out the discs so they can be cut out with the largest cutter from the set. Place these discs onto greaseproof in between two trays (it is better to use the back of the trays as they are flatter) place two heavy weights on the trays and rest in the fridge for 10 minutes. After they have been rested use a fork to dock the discs not going near the edges. Place back between the trays and cook in the oven at 180 degrees until they are golden brown (about ten minutes) once they are cooked they should be placed on a cooling wire on top of the rational oven. This job should be the last one before service, any discs that are left over after service should be discarded.

## Part 4: Confit Potatoes

1KG Ratte Potatoes
Duck Fat
3 Sprigs Thyme, 1 Bay leaf, 20 coriander seeds, 20 peppercorns and 3 star anise.

Place enough Duck Fat in a pot to cover the potatoes on the stove and melt slowly. When its melted add the potatoes and the rest of the ingredients which should tied in muslin. Confit slowly on the edge of the stove until the potatoes are just cooked and no more. Once they are cooked they should be removed from the fat immediately and cooled as quickly as possible. Once they are cooled they can be sliced thinly and stored in a container (you should only cut as much as you need for service)

### Part 5: Julienne of Speck Ham

Slice the frozen speck ham on the slicer and cut into strips. Cook the bacon over a medium heat in a dry non-stick pan (no oil is needed) place in a chinois to drain of any fat.

### Assembly

Place some warm confit onions onto a disc and then place the confit potatoes around the disc so it forms a complete circle. Place three slices of the camembert on next (these should not hang over the edge or the tarte) add some speck ham and sit on the top of the oven until it is called away. Then place on the centre of the plate and place lightly dressed leaves on top. Serve with a warm truffle and leek vinaigrette.

*Head Chef: David Williams*
**Greywalls, Muirfield, Gullane, East Lothian. EH31 2EG**
(also see entry page 31)

# Rack of Lamb with New Season, Garlic Savarin, Tomato Confit, Crushed Courgettes, Stuffed Courgette Blossom, Lamb Jus.
### (Serves 4)

## Ingredients:

1 Pair of Lamb Best Ends French trimmed
1 tbs. Olive Oil
20g Butter
30 Cloves new season Garlic, peeled
6 Egg Yolks
1 tbs. Softened Butter
6 Basil leaves
8 Petals of Tomato Confit
250g Spinach
4 Courgette Flowers
300g Young Courgettes
1 Clove Garlic in skin
100ml Olive Oil
Salt and Pepper
200ml Lamb Jus
10g Butter

**For the Flower Stuffing:**

1 Carrot
2 Shallots
100g Celeriac
100g Leek
4 Petals of Tomato Confit
100g Cooked chopped Spinach
2tbs.Chicken Mousse
1tsp.Chopped Chives
1 tsp. Chopped Chervil
1 tbs. Olive Oil
Salt and Pepper

### For the Flowers:

Clean peel and cut the vegetables into 5mm dice. Sweat in olive oil until tender but not coloured. Cool. Cut the tomato confit into similar sized dice. Fold all the ingredients into the chicken mousse and season. Place into a piping bag and fill the flowers. Steam for 5-8 mins. Keep warm.

### For the Garlic Savarin

Cook the garlic in three changes of water adding a pinch of salt into the final stage. Place into a liquidizer and puree with the egg yolks and butter. Pass through a fine strainer and add chopped basil leaves. Pipe into savarin moulds and steam for 5-8 mins. Keep warm.

### For the Crushed Courgettes

Cut courgettes into 5mm dice. Heat olive oil in a shallow saucepan. Add garlic to flavour the oil  but do not colour the garlic. Add the courgettes, season, then cover the pan and allow to cook gently for 5-10 mins, being careful to maintain the colour. Remove garlic, skin and chop, add back to the courgettes and crush with a fork. Keep warm.

### For the Lamb.

Season lamb all over with salt and pepper. Heat the olive oil and colour the best ends all over. Place in a hot oven (220⁰) for approx. 6-8 mins, remove and add butter. Baster while the butter foams. Allow to rest in a warm place for 15-20 mins.

### For the Spinach

Cook quickly in foaming butter and season.

### To Serve.

Place a savarin on each of your plates. Fill the centres with spinach and top with two warm tomato confit petals. Place the crushed courgettes in a ring next to the savarin. Top with cutlets carved from the rack. Place a flower next to the lamb. Heat lamb jus and whisk in the butter. Coat the flower with sauce and drizzle the rest around the plate. Serve.

*Head Chef: Trevor Brooks*
**Kinnaird, Kinnaird Estate, By Dunkeld, Perthshire. PH8 0LB**
(also see entry page 27)

# Pan fried fillet of Wild Sea Trout on roast Garlic and Lemon scented Cous Cous, Estate Chanterelles and Lobster Foam

(Serves 4)

### Ingredients:

1 cup Cous Cous
2 cloves of garlic
Zest and juice of 1 lemon
1 litre Chicken stock
Parsley
Salt and Pepper

4 x 6oz Sea Trout pin boned and scaled
Broccoli, 1 head florets blanched
Baby Spinach
Asparagus, 20 spears blanched
Chanterelles, 20 good size
Avruga Caviar
Chervil to garnish

### Method for Cous Cous:

Reduce chicken stock with thyme, garlic, lemon zest and juice. Add to cous cous and cover with cling film for 10 minutes. Stir cous cous and add chopped parsley and adjust to taste.

### Method:

Warm through the blanched vegetables in a butter emulsion and drain off. Season and pan fry the Sea Trout in oil and butter until the skin is crispy and golden. Sautee Chanterelles and drain onto a tray. Warm lobster veloute. Wilt off the Spinach and drain on a tray with a j cloth.

### To Serve:

Place cous cous in a pastry cutter in the middle of the plate and place spinach on top. Place Sea Trout on top of Spinach. Arrange 5 florets of Broccoli, 5 Chanterelles and Asparagus resting on Broccoli around the plate. Blitz veloute with hand blitzer and drizzle around the plate. Finish with a teaspoon quenelle of Avruga and Chervil and serve.

*Head Chef: Jonny Greer*
**Ballathie, Kinclaven, By Stanley, Perthshire. PH1 4QN**
(also see entry page 45)

# Panache of Roasted Scallops and Foie Gras, Sauce Sauternes

### Serves 4

## Ingredients

6 x XL Diver Caught Scallops
4 x 50g Escalopes of Foie Gras
6 x Baby Beetroot Cooked and Peeled
12 x Baby Leeks, Blanched
1 x Courgette Finely diced
200g Small rocket leaves
50g Butter
5 x Tablespoon Chicken Stock

Fig & Mango Chutney
50g Butter
2 x Shallots Diced
10 x Dried Figs
50ml Apple Juice
15ml Balsamic Vinegar
15ml Sherry Vinegar
1 tsp Dijon Mustard
1 Clove Crushed Garlic
50g Raisins
60g Caster Sugar

### For the Chutney

Melt butter in a pan, add diced shallot and cook for 2 minutes without colour. Add the other ingredients except the sugar and cook slowly until all the moisture has gone, transfer mix to a robot coupe, add the sugar and puree, check seasoning and set aside.

Sauce Sauternes
2 x Shallots finely sliced
4 x Button Mushrooms, finely sliced
50g Unsalted Butter
150ml Sauternes
100 ml Chicken Stock
100ml Scallop Stock
150 ml Double Cream

### For the Sauce

Sweat shallots and mushrooms in 50g butter until softened without colour, add sauternes and bring to the boil reduce by half. Add chicken stock and bring to the boil, reduce by half again, add scallop stock, bring to the boil and reduce by half. Add the double cream and bring to the boil and simmer for 5 minutes, season, pass through sieve into a clean pan.

### To Serve

Cut the baby beetroot in half, season, warm up in a knob of butter and 1 tablespoon chicken stock. Cut baby leeks into 4, season; warm up in a knob of butter and 2 tablespoons of chicken stock. Melt a knob of butter and add 2 tablespoon chicken stock, add diced courgette and rocket leaves, cook and season. Cut Scallops in half, heat up 2 non-stick pans, season scallops and cook for about 30 seconds each side, depending on the thickness. Season and cook the Foie Gras on both sides, keeping it nice and pink in the middle. Gently warm sauternes sauce and chutney.

### To Dress

On 4 heated plates, place 3 scallops overlapping on one side, criss-cross 6 pieces of baby leek down the centre of the plate, place the rocket and courgette diced and baby beetroot by the other side of the leeks, top with the Foie Gras and a quenelle of chutney, pour sauce around and serve.

*Head Chef: Iain McNaught*
**Roman Camp Country House, Callander, Perthshire. FK17 8BG**
(also see entry page 23)

# STEVENSONS

## SCOTLAND'S
## GOOD HOTEL AND FOOD BOOK
## 2007

*Order Form:* **Alan Stevenson Publications**
**Fala, 20 West Cairn Crescent, Penicuik,**
**Midlothian EH26 0AR**
**Tel: 01968 678015**
**Fax: 01968 679898**
**E-mail: alan@stevensons-scotland.com**

Date: ..................................... Please mail ............... Copies of

**Stevensons, Scotland's Good Hotel and Food Book, 2007.**

Your Name: ...............................................................................

Address: ...................................................................................

........................................................ Postcode: .........................

| Retail Price | 1 Book | 2-5 Books | 6 + Books |
|---|---|---|---|
| United Kingdom | £8.00 | £7.00 each | p.o.a. |
| USA only | $18.00 | $14.00 each | p.o.a. |
| Canada only | $20.00 | $15.00 each | p.o.a. |
| Europe | £8.00 | £7.00 each | p.o.a. |
| Euro Zone | €14.00 | €12.00 each | p.o.a. |
| Outside Europe | £12.00 | £10.00 each | p.o.a. |

| Post & Packaging | 1 Book | 2-5 Books | 6 + Books |
|---|---|---|---|
| United Kingdom | £2.00 | £5.00 | p.o.a. |
| USA/Canada | $9.00 | $11.00 | p.o.a. |
| Europe | £4.00 | £7.50 | p.o.a. |
| Euro Zone | €6.50 | €10.00 | p.o.a. |
| Outside Europe | £5.00 | £4.00 | p.o.a. |

**All orders outwith United Kingdom consigned by airmail. Payment in pounds sterling, please, payable to Alan Stevenson Publications - alternatively online at www.stevensons-scotland.com**

No. of Copies: ...... at £/$/€ .............. each.  Total £/$/€ ....................

Post & Packaging  Total £/$/€ ....................

**I enclose a Cheque/Bank Draft**  Total £/$/€ ....................

## Hotels continued

## Restaurants listed alphabetically by name

INDEX

# Hotels listed alphabetically by name

See contents page 4 for list of Trade Sponsors.